THE FI

OF MORIA

THE FIVE STAGES
OF MORIA

ELIKA ANSARI

palavro
PUBLISHING

The Five Stages of Moria
By Elika Ansari

© Elika Ansari

ISBN: 9781912092048

First published in 2022

Published by Palavro, an imprint of
the Arkbound Foundation (Publishers)

Arkbound is a social enterprise that aims to promote social inclusion, community development and artistic talent. It sponsors publications by disadvantaged authors and covers issues that engage wider social concerns. Arkbound fully embraces sustainability and environmental protection. It endeavours to use material that is renewable, recyclable or sourced from sustainable forest.

Arkbound
Rogart Street Campus
4 Rogart Street
Glasgow, G40 2AA

www.arkbound.com

Disclaimer

All the stories in this book, though mainly inspired by real events, conversations and states of mind, have been fictionalised and names have been altered where relevant. The intention is to preserve anonymity but also, very importantly, to give the author creative freedom in order to paint a more comprehensive, generalised picture of what Moria refugee camp was really like.

Preface

Let me begin by confessing that I am not a refugee. I emigrated from Iran to the U.K., where my father was already a resident, at the age of seven. A year later, I moved to Spain, where I settled down with my family until I turned 18. An aspiration for further studies, work and a genuine curiosity for the world I had yet to discover swept me away to a life of permanent expatriation. You could say my status as a legal immigrant granted me the ability to choose that life.

For some observers, the lines between the two categories – immigrant and refugee – might be somewhat blurred. To their credit, there are indeed a number of attributes in the lives of both refugees and immigrants that we can claim to have in common – like the initiation rites we go through to fit into our host nations and the persistent language and cultural barriers we face. Or the sense of non-belonging, . being labelled as an 'Other' – someone both intrinsically exotic and suspiciously menacing all at once – or the challenges that come with defining our own identity, as someone who is never quite here nor there, but always somewhere in between. There is also that familiar, yet hazy, memory of a home we perhaps cannot return to – at least not spiritually – because, even if we did have the option to physically return one day, there would be no sense of home left to appease us.

However, there are also fundamental differences between refugees and immigrants that cannot and should not be glossed over. For me, the most significant difference is highlighted in the journey. I don't remember much about my journey out of my native Iran. It involved some disorderly packing, visas being issued, passports being hastily stamped, an uneventful plane ride and a nonchalant customs agent.

For a refugee or asylum seeker, on the other hand, the journey is not something easily forgotten. It is precisely the journey, fraught with perils, that leads people to put their lives in the hands of complete strangers and has the potential to make or break them. It is the dangers that refugees and asylum seekers face, either when crossing the sea in a wobbly rubber boat that threatens to sink at any moment, or when trekking more miles than any human being ever should on foot, that misleads many of them into believing that, once they arrive at the European border, the hardest part is over.

Unfortunately, that is when their idea of a better life is replaced with the unimaginable reality of living in a refugee camp. Access to basic rights, like education, healthcare, or adequate food and shelter are certainly not provided on equal terms for immigrants and native Europeans. Nevertheless, they were still things I can say that, as an immigrant, I was able to take for granted while I was growing up. I would have most likely continued to take them for granted had I not taken the decision to step out of my comfort zone – where wilful ignorance had kept me sheltered for too long – and become acquainted with refugees and their lives.

In 2015, while living my comfortable life as a postgraduate student in Brussels, I decided to begin volunteering with an organisation that offered befriending and outreach activities to asylum seekers. The experience changed my life. I came to realise that there were others just like me, with the same chestnut brown eyes and mocha-coloured skin, facing similar struggles to learn one or several foreign languages while trying not to forget their mother tongue. They were pretty much like me in every respect, aside from the vital fact that they had been forced to live at the mercy of a dysfunctional asylum system. This often meant they had to live in inhuman conditions for longer than our universal conscience would care to admit. Meeting dozens of people from Afghanistan, Iran and other countries, whose lives hung by a thread and whose daily existence was a fight for survival, was what finally broke me out of my cocooned existence.

2015 was also the year the European media adopted the term *'Migration Crisis'*, when more than one million refugees arrived at EU borders asking for protection. The public discourse surrounding migrants in general, and refugees in particular, became more distorted and confusing. One minute the mass media empathised with the figure of the poor, defenceless refugee for all the wrong reasons; the next they were tagged as a threat, an encroachment or extension of Islamist extremism, to be shunned or feared.

Furthermore, by conflating the terms *'migrant'* and *'refugee'* or *'asylum seeker'*, the media was telling the public not to jump to conclusions about the status of these people. They would be called *'refugees'* if and when they succeeded in their asylum application and therefore earned the label of a *'refugee'* alongside the protection of their European patrons.

Skimming through article after article about the so-called *crisis*, I couldn't help but feel that every news outlet depicted refugee narratives with such carelessness and oversimplification, that even someone with prior knowledge and contact with refugee communities could not even begin to imagine what conditions were like in the 'hotspots' at the edge of the European Union. Not knowing meant not being able to do more.

I came to Greece in May 2017 with the intention to help. My first duty station as a humanitarian aid worker was just outside of Athens, in a small refugee camp, home to about 30 single mothers and their children – the majority of whom were from Syria, Afghanistan and Iran. I spent eight unforgettable months growing close to some of the most wonderful women I have had the privilege to know. Their stories varied. Some had fled abusive relationships or circumstances; others had found the courage to escape a raging war, and others still had left with the hope of offering their children the opportunities they never had themselves. But what they all manifested, with no exception, was an unprecedented degree of strength and resilience. They taught me so much about endurance and the ability to not let your past life define your present; a lesson I am eternally grateful for. I grew so close to these families; in fact, that when it was time for them to move on , I couldn't help but feel they were taking a part of me with them. A part I could never retrieve, because the life I had allowed myself to grow to love was shattering. As selfish as that may sound, I could not bring myself to stay and pick up the pieces. When they left, so did I.

My next destination was the island of Lesbos. This first time, my stay here was quite short, since the non-governmental organisation (NGO) I worked for had its funding cut unexpectedly. But the time I spent on the island, however brief, gave me the foundation I would later count on when coming back to stay for another three years.

Next stop was Northern Greece. I settled in a small city called Ioannina and alternated between four of the surrounding refugee camps in neighbouring villages, in what is known as the Epirus region. The Epirus region is situated close to the Albanian border, thus offering glimpses of the possibility of a gateway into another world to those stuck on the Greek side of the barrier.

Few asylum seekers can actually fathom a future for themselves in Greece, as it is known in their common imagination to be a struggling nation with an unstable economy and little support to spare for people in need of protection. In fact, passing their asylum interview and being officially recognised as a legal refugee brings mixed feelings for the vast majority. Though the refugee status gives people the indefinite right to remain, work and live independently in the country, they are coerced to exercise that right within a short time span, meaning they have only a few months after the reception of their refugee status before their cash assistance is cut off and they are forced to leave the camp or refugee shelter. With little or no access to jobs or education, it is not realistic to expect hundreds of thousands of asylum seekers and refugees to become self-sufficient in such a restricted time frame and thus, many choose not to make Greece their long-term home.

So, it is safe to assume that the asylum seekers in Northern Greece were either just passively waiting and wilting in the shadow of that other world beyond the barrier; or, for those who still had some fight left in them, they were actively looking for a pathway across the border and beyond, into countries that had the means to make more fulfilling promises to their community.

I stayed in Northern Greece for five months before the opportunity came for me to return to Lesbos in May 2018; this time to work in Moria.

Since my arrival in Greece, I had heard so much about the notorious Moria camp. Situated just off the coast of Turkey in the Northern Aegean Sea, the island was a first point of entry for asylum seekers coming to Europe.

The camp was a former prison-turned-refugee facility elevated next to Moria village, located near Mytilene – the main town on the island of Lesbos. Before it burned down in September 2020, Moria was known as the biggest refugee camp in Europe and described by its residents in news reports as a "living hell," "the worst refugee camp on Earth" and an "ideal breeding ground for the rapid spread" of the coronavirus, among other things. After the time I spent there, I could certainly vouch for each of these descriptions.

Moria was built as a transitory camp to accommodate a maximum capacity of 3,000 people for a period of a few days, prior to their being sent to the mainland for continued asylum procedures. However, in my almost three years of working in the camp, I witnessed anywhere between 5,000 and 22,000 asylum seekers being crammed into unsanitary spaces.

After the signing of the EU-Turkey deal in 2016 and the implementation of the containment policy on the Greek islands, the waiting period before being transferred to the mainland also began to gradually increase from weeks to months, and even years for some. This meant more and more people were forced to live in overcrowded, dehumanising conditions for extended periods of time, where even the most basic human rights were a struggle. Legal assistance, access to healthcare, water and sanitation facilities, electricity during the night, heating in bitingly cold winters, fans during the sweltering summers – even access to decent food, clothes, or adequate shelter were all considered luxuries for the residents of Moria.

In my time there, I saw too many asylum seekers come and go. I saw people in shock, struggling to take in the deception of their European dream. I witnessed people break down, with their frustrations peaking, and saw them verbally lash out at each other or aid workers, including myself. I witnessed these people in their worst states of mind, with a readiness to surrender the fight of daily living. And finally, they ended up accepting the circumstances, unjust as they may have been, and just pulled out all the stops to make the best of a terrible situation.

At first thought, I considered how these transitions in the refugees' states of mind may have been the result of their different personalities. But time, experience and further reflection helped me reach the hypothesis that I was perceiving a glimpse of the phases that human beings go through to deal with grief or trauma – the trauma here being the harrowing experience of Moria refugee camp.

I came to see patterns of what was happening to these people: five stages that every person seemed to go through from the point of their arrival at the camp to their assent of the status quo. So, I modelled this book loosely around Elizabeth Kubler Ross and David Kessler's *Five Stages of Grief*.[1] Stage 1: *shock*; stage 2: *anger*; stage 3: *guilt*; stage 4: *depression*; and stage 5: *acceptance*.

It was not easy for me to find a way to depict the amalgam of stories and voices I encountered in these three years. It did not escape me that human experiences are not homogenous, and therefore it would be somewhat inaccurate, and perhaps fictional, for me to try to capture and neatly categorise their stories into these *five stages*. But there was something about the horrors of Moria that brought people together and made them form a community that perhaps otherwise would not

1   Kubler-Ross, Elisabeth. *On Death and Dying: What the Dying Have to Teach Doctors, Nurses, Clergy and Their Own Families.* Scribner, 2014.

have existed. There was a commonality that, despite their different backgrounds, made them live through this new experience in a very collective, distinguishable and almost predictable way.

Surely enough, I cannot claim to speak for the tens of thousands of people who have experienced Moria in their own individual ways, or for those who have dealt with the hardship of life in the camp while carrying the burden of their pasts, nor would I ever dream of doing so. And by no means do I wish to paint such remarkable and diverse communities in bleak brush strokes of black and white; the media does enough of that already. Though a good part of my humanitarian work involved engaging with the camp's community or, in a way, attempting to understand the plights that affect the psychology of asylum seekers in Moria, I admit that I am by no means a psychologist nor a mental health professional. These are just my personal observations as someone who had ample opportunities to interact with people on a daily basis for a prolonged period of time. Someone who saw some of these people's mental health status go from bad to worse. Someone who met too many asylum seekers arriving in Moria for the first time, knowing what they were going through and knowing what was yet in store for them, having seen it happen to so many before them, but not having the heart to tell them that the worst was yet to come.

For these reasons and many others, I chose to write this book as a work of fiction. Doing so gave me the liberty to bypass the restrictions of the factual portrayals and first-person accounts required of the non-fiction genre. It gave me the creative licence to extrapolate conversations from one context and place them in another, switch points of view, and attempt to elicit a more emotional response by using all the creative tools at my disposal.

However, this does not mean that the people in these stories were not real; that the challenges they faced were not trying or authentic enough, or that the seething despair they were made to endure was not genuine. I even chose to write myself in as a character, 'Maryam', in an attempt to demonstrate the camp's all-encompassing and indiscriminate impact on those less directly associated with the camp's ramifications, such as aid workers and volunteers. Because, at the end of the day, nobody was immune to Moria.

Even in the midst of writing this book, I was horrified to read news articles about the Greek government deploying hundreds of security forces to implement detention centres or closed camps on the Greek islands. I glimpsed reports of asylum seekers and aid workers, my former colleagues, being deliberately targeted by fascist groups. I heard bemusing stories of thousands of people crammed into tents and caravans, being unreasonably advised to practice social distancing due to the advent of the COVID-19 global pandemic.

The world turned its back on Moria and other reception centres for too long, while the impact on those trapped in these camps appeared to be at its worst. They continue to turn their backs on them, when differentiating between brands of refugees, races of refugees, giving out selective support and charity to those nearer to their own backyards.

I hope that by choosing to portray the subject through this specific genre I manage to transport readers, mind and soul, even if only minimally, to that other reality that existed – and still exists – in parallel to theirs.

STAGE 1: SHOCK

In this stage, the world becomes meaningless and overwhelming. Life makes no sense. We are in a state of shock and denial. We go numb. We wonder how we can go on, if we can go on, why we should go on. We try to find a way to simply get through each day.[2]

David Kessler

2   "Five Stages of Grief by Elisabeth Kubler Ross & David Kessler." Grief.com, grief.com/the-five-stages-of-grief/.

1.1 Mahdi

I am falling. Falling down a deep, dark ditch. It feels like I've been falling for hours and there is no end in sight. It's so cold, I can't feel my hands or feet. Not even my face.

What is this place? Where am I? I stop for a moment; just one moment. Now I am suspended in mid-air. Somehow, that feels worse than falling. At least if I am falling, I'd be getting somewhere. Like this, I am just waiting. *And waiting. And waiting...*But for what?

My eyes begin to adjust to the darkness. Unknown shapes cast shadows, ominous contours of something or nothing. Nothing about this place looks or feels familiar. Except—

There is something down there, but I can't see. It's still too dark.

Is this what dying feels like?

Splash. I hear water. *Clank.* There is something over there! *Splash.* What's happening?

Whatever force is holding me up in the air suddenly releases my weight. I drop out of the sky like a bird with no wings.

CLANK.

SPLASH.

I'm in a rubber boat in the middle of the sea. A storm is brewing. There are 70 of us – men, women and children – crammed next to each other. My heart hammers against my chest as bolts of lightning break through the dark sky. The muttering around me shatters into women screaming and children crying.

Fast forward a few seconds, and I am throwing up grimy water from deep inside my core. Where's it all coming from? It soaks my clothes, drenches me to the bone. It's not exactly cold. It's numbing. It's everywhere.

Make it stop. Please. I can't swim. Help! *Please*. I can't swim. Someone hears me.

Hello? It's still dark, but there is something here. Someone. I can *feel* her. Eyes. Big, brown, moist. And familiar, so familiar. They are gazing at me. No, more like boring through me, suddenly making me feel exposed; naked. A trembling courses through my body. I wrap my arms around my chest to shield my skin from intrusive eyes. So much has changed now. I am not who I used to be.

"*Madar jan.*"

My mother looks at me, but she doesn't really see me. It is as if she is gazing beyond me at a scene I am not privy to.

There are mountains of sand all around us, with hints of a sparkling sea on the horizon. She turns her back to me and busies herself, washing dishes, in the manner she always does when I do something wrong and she doesn't want to talk about it.

There is a breeze and the sound of dishes clanking and splashing water. "*Madar jan....*" She can't hear me, or if she does, she chooses not to listen.

"*Madar*, I am here. I made it," I try to tell her, still keeping my distance. *Splash. Clank. Splash.*

"Look at me!" I yell. My voice belongs to someone else. Her absence makes muscles tense in anger. I jolt towards her figure and grab her by the shoulders. "Look into my eyes!" I demand. But without turning around, she crumbles at my touch, like a sandcastle squashed by a little boy who pretended not to know any better.

It's dark again. The waves break against the shore. They crash hard against rocks and harder against the earth, threatening to engulf me. *Splash. Clank. Splash.* I'm alone again. Just me and the vast, grey sea, threatening to swallow anyone who crosses its path.

Nothing but black sand and grey water. The waves are getting closer.

I stop fighting it. *Splash. Clank. Splash.* I can feel its coldness encroaching on my skin. *Splash. Clank. Splash.* The stink of saltwater makes my stomach churn. I let it take me. *Splash. Clank. Splash.* It burns my lungs. I can't breathe. *I can't breathe.*

I wake up with a start on the kerb, panting. Sweat beads cover my forehead. I wheeze for a moment, still not sure whether I am in another dream or whether I can actually breathe. The cement ground is cold and invasive against my skin.

I glance around, trying to remember where I am. Waves are breaking gently against the port. People are coming and going, some sounding familiar, others speaking languages I have never even heard in movies.

It's all coming back to me now.

Location: a Greek harbour across the Aegean Sea with 70 other refugees. Status: Alive, but only barely.

I glance down at my phone. So many scratches and cracks on the screen. It's a wonder it's still working after all it has been through.

I feel like I haven't slept in days. I stretch and propel myself up to sit with my back against a dusty bin, lifting my head up to get a better view of these strange people. Tourists with tropical shirts and bamboo sandals. I have no idea where they are from.

There's this snotty-faced kid with dirty blond hair standing a few feet away, staring at me from behind his Scooby-Doo glasses.

"*Boro, bacha.*" I shoo him away with my hand, but he just keeps staring. Or maybe he's looking through me, or past me, like my mother did before she turned to sand. I make a face.

Not an aggressive one, but overt enough to scare away any European kid who's seen refugees on the news lately. We're not a pretty sight.

"Josef," his mother waves the boy over, and he shuffles off.

I pull my black hoodie over my lank hair and hope that concealing half of my face will somehow make me less visible to the rest of the tourists. Then, propping myself up, I rise to my feet, still light-headed. My mind jerks back to the dream – no, *memory* – of that rubber boat.

Back and forth. Left and right. All I see are blurs and shadows. Flashing contours. Disfigured half-faces. Fragmented voices.

"Mummy, why is the sky roaring?"

"Help, someone! Anyone!"

"God, are you there? Can you hear me?"

"My baby, where's my baby?"

"Help him, please. He can't swim!"

"There, at a distance. Do you see it? I think there's something. Yes, there's a flashing light! Is it – yes, it must be. The shore is right there!"

Hope, when you most need it, has a way of flickering in the darkest corners.

I feel queasy. I am standing alongside tens of other Afghans, waiting for the bus. A whiff of Marlboro smoke suddenly slaps me across the head. The smell of it is like oxygen for my cells.

I emerge from under my hoodie, and my eyes dart around to see a middle-aged man a few steps away, puffing out clouds of smoke like he enjoys the very thought of polluting the air around his face. On instinct, I reach into my jeans' pocket and fish out my own pack of cigarettes, but I am disappointed to see that they are soggy from the seawater.

I get such an urge to smoke at that moment, as if oxygen has been sucked out of my lungs and I have no way to inhale it back in. As if I am back in the middle of that black sea, swallowing muddy water.

Before I know it, my legs grow a life of their own and walk over to the man.

"Could you spare a drag for a poor, young addict, *kaka jan?*" I flash a cheeky grin. He raises one eyebrow.

"Aren't you a little too young to be smoking, boy?"

"Never too young to enjoy life," I stand my ground, still grinning.

The *kaka* sighs, takes the cigarette out of his mouth and hands it over to me. Intense relief rushes through my veins as I take my first drag in what feels like forever. My lungs open up, as if I had been holding my breath all this time. As if I had just spit out the last bout of that disgusting seawater that almost drowned me.

Then a large, imposing woman suddenly appears next to us. She clicks her tongue at the man who must be her husband, then shoots me a look through narrow eyes. "What would your father say if he saw you smoking, *bacha?*"

"Lucky for me, he's dead, *khala jan,*" I say flatly. I take another drag and blow the smoke over my head.

"*Tuba, Astaghfurillah!* Repentance! Shame on you!" She tightens her mud-brown scarf over her round face and pulls her husband away by the arm.

A little to the right, a young woman in a white headscarf sits on the kerb. She has a little boy resting in her arms with his head draping over her shoulder. She has a daughter too, sitting quietly next to her, as well-behaved as all little girls should be. But no husband in sight. Unlike the woman who just grumbled at me, this one has a kind, gentle face. Her eyes are a silky, honey shade of brown. Her lips are red and kind – like my mother's, before she forgot how to smile.

I take another drag and inhale the smoke entirely. I let my gaze wander back to the sea and shudder. Though the water is calm now, it still makes me feel sick to my stomach.

Splash. Clank. Splash.

* * * * *

A bus pulls over. It looks like our own buses in Afghanistan: rickety and old, yet somehow still standing tall. Even the driver, a portly old man with a massive belly and heavy pelts, has that same indifferent expression as our own drivers.

A line of refugees is already forming in front of the bus. I hurry to place myself almost at the front, just behind the *kaka,* who gave me the cigarette, and his nagging wife. The driver sizes us up, holding my gaze with his steel eyes for a few more seconds than I would like. I don't flinch. He then gives a brisk nod of the head to signal we can start boarding.

I flick my cigarette away and hop on to take a window seat near the front row. The seats are worn and covered with frayed bits of fabric. Their damp, mouldy smell makes me feel light-headed.

It's not long before the bus fills up with our party – mostly Afghans, but also a few Arabs – anxious to be reassigned to a new home.

I let my body slump into the seat and let out a sigh of relief that I have been holding in for days. The bus whizzes past hilly landscapes to one side and stretches of sea to the other.

In our village in Kunduz, all the boys in my class sneak out of the madrasa every day. Today, the old Mullah follows us and catches us puffing smoke over our heads behind the dumpsters. The other boys manage to run away in time, but I trip over a root and fall, scraping my knee. The old goat catches up with me, pulls me up by the collar and almost chokes me with the hem of my shirt. He spits out something, then hits me over the side of my head with the rifle he casually carries around like an extension of his hand.

"You are here by Allah's will to be trained to perform Jihad. Don't you forget that, o bacha," the words fly out of his soiled beard. He's probably been growing it since he was my age. I bleed through my forehead, and I can't see straight for weeks until the wound starts to scar. But if I had to do it again, I would, without a second thought.

I press two fingers gently against my temple. Thinking about Afghanistan always makes my scar prickle.

The little boy, who was sleeping in his mother's arms, whimpers and pulls on her robes.

"I'm hungry."

His mother, lost in thought, continues to gaze contemplatively out of the window with her honey-coloured eyes.

"*Maman*, I'm hungry," the boy moans again.

The boy's sister, who could not have been more than three or four years older than him, scolds her little brother.

"*Shh* Mohsen, leave Mummy alone."

It's so easy to recognise them; the kids who stopped being kids a long time ago.

The boy pouts at his sister, tilts his face away from her and crosses his arms grumpily.

For the rest of the way, everyone on the bus is silent. It's almost eerie. No one is saying a thing; not even the ones who travelled together are speaking to each other. The air is heavy with tension. Something is wrong with this whole scene. Surely, we can relax a bit now that we have made it this far? I mean, who could have said for sure we'd make it to Europe at all?

We could still be stuck in Turkey, waiting by the shore day after day, praying for the time to cross over. Or worse still, we could be lying at the bottom of the sea, struck by a premature death like thousands of others before us.

"My friend."

A skinny Syrian man with black, ruffled hair, who appears to be in his mid-20s, finally breaks the silence – one of the few non-Afghans in our party. He leans forward on the edge of his seat, then stands up for a moment. Holding up his oversized jeans against his bony waistline with one hand, he frantically waves the other hand in the air to get the driver's attention.

"Where? Here. Where?" he tries in broken English. The driver ignores him, adjusts the rear-view mirror and continues on track.

Without warning, an acrid stench seeps into the bus, ambushing my senses. I twitch my nose and grimace. There's that queasy feeling again.

"*Ay Khuda,* what *is* that?" I hear a woman say, to no one in particular, as she tugs her head scarf around her face to shield her mouth and nose from the smell.

The bus takes a sharp left turn at the roundabout, bouncing on the bumpy road. The driver seems to be in a hurry to get rid of our group.

The stench is getting stronger. Passengers mumble disgruntledly, disgusted. As we draw nearer to our destination, its source becomes apparent: grimy sewage water is being pumped out of the camp through large pipes.

From a distance, I can already spot endless rows of makeshift tents in the groves on a steep slope. There are hundreds, maybe even thousands, of displaced refugees queueing up here and there.

Our bus turns off the road, where another navy-blue police bus is parked, just below the dirt track that runs parallel to the perimeter fence of the camp.

There is something graffitied on the decaying cement wall just up ahead. 'Welcome to Moria.' But the word 'Moria' is crossed out and preceded by the word 'Prison' instead, written in faded, black letters.

My heart sinks. I try to swallow the lump in my throat. A quick scan around reveals the other passengers to be expressionless; no one so much as gasps at the sight of the wall. Could it be that they didn't notice? Or perhaps they could not make out the writing?

I'm surprised I remember this much of the English alphabet. English was strictly forbidden in the *madrasa*; they called it the language of the invaders. Instead, the weekly curriculum included other life lessons you probably don't get on this side of the world, like how to properly hold a gun.

A little farther on, and the tall, chain-link gates to the camp are easily shoved open by the security guard. The bus enters the camp and finally pulls over at another gate, another fenced barrier; the pathway to inauguration for new arrivals.

The bus driver rises to his feet, turns back to face the passengers and claps his hands together.

"Έλα έξω," he commands huskily. Then, seeing no reaction from the dumbfounded passengers, he begins to yell something in Greek until we all rush off the bus against our will.

I take a reluctant look around the refugee camp, at the

thousands more refugees bustling around, crowding around gates or forming line after crooked line. The way people shout over each other, each in their own colourful dialects, reminds me of my hometown.

All around me, small children and women poke their heads out of their tattered tents or compact caravans.

"My friend," the Arab man with the broken English approaches, cigarette casually dangling from his mouth as he speaks again, this time to me.

"This – where?"

His question triggers a moment of instant registration in my mind, where things suddenly fall into place, like a wisp of fog being lifted from in front of my eyes.

"This is Moria," I say, trying to keep my voice steady.

The man's eyes grow wide. His mouth opens even wider, giving way for his hand-rolled cigarette to fall out of his mouth. I catch it in mid-air, between my thumb and index finger, and take a drag myself. The nicotine rush has little effect this time.

The man no longer seems to see me. Instead, he sees what I cannot unsee. That imaginary veil of victory is lifting. The thought that the worst is over is exposed as a dangerous lie. A lie we told and retold ourselves and everyone else who asked, in order to get us here in one piece.

I can't see the sea anymore, but I can feel every one of its waves. Breaking against the shore. Rhythmically.

Splash. Clank. Splash.

We are home.

1.2 Maryam

With my vest on full display, its bright red logo confirms my allegiance to the world of humanitarian aid workers. I swerve the tall, uninviting gates of Moria camp and enter through the smaller, open side gate. There, behind a sheet of glass, reclines the sulky receptionist with his gleaming bald head.

"Name?" he grunts from behind his protective vitrine, barely looking up to meet my gaze.

"Mr Panagiotis, it's me," I force a smile, not unkindly, but not wholeheartedly either. I've been coming here every day for more than a year. How hard can it be to learn my name? "I work in the clinic across the street."

He grunts again and holds out his hand through the gap. I sigh and fish my badge out of my vest pocket. Even if he does remember me, he is not going to do me any favours.

Mr Panagiotis automatically types my name into his computer system and gives me clearance in the form of a dismissive wave of the hand. I hurriedly pin my badge to my breast pocket to avoid any further identity probes and step through.

I am in.

The concrete road ahead stretches long and wide open. From a short distance, I can see hundreds of women in colourful hijabs running errands in the early hours of the morning. There are men in faded jeans queueing with files and papers in their grips and children in oversized flip-flops playing catch.

Around me, there is a unique soundtrack, a clamour of voices in baffling dialects of Farsi, Dari, Arabic, and a unique mix of French and Lingala.

I can't put my finger on it, but there is something in this camp that feels both familiar and unfamiliar. Something that reminds me of a life that once existed.

There is something about the people here, their greetings, the lingering aromas in the air that allow me to travel back in time to a childhood that I never experienced in full.

I was only seven when I left Tehran for Europe, so I can't claim to remember very much. But sometimes, fragments come back to me: silk headscarves and clanking gold and silver chains in the narrow alleys of Persian *bazaars*; exhilarated children running around *Parke Mellat*, perhaps a little version of me among them; the rich scent of onions and saffron on my grandmother's pruny hands, wet from the day's cooking and washing.

"*Naan-e dagho garm.* Get your hot naans!"

The fragrance of freshly baked *naan* bread wafts through the morning sky.

"*Qabali pallaw!* Get it hot, get it fresh!"

Moria vendors yell over one another, attempting to sell what they promise to be the best goods on all the island – anything and everything from grilled chicken to *qabalii pallaw*, *bolani*, macaroni with minced beef, Persian stew to hot chicken soup.

I pace along the main road of the camp, my gait resolute, but my mouth relaxed and my eyes receptive. Before long, my gaze fixates on the throng of asylum seekers flocking behind the various other gates and fences inside the camp.

There are people queueing to see a doctor, others to report an issue with their cash cards and others still for breakfast. Whatever their objective or circumstances, everybody queues for something.

"*Salam alaykum*, Maryam *khanoom*," a cheery man with a thick moustache yells. He waves to me over the clamour of the throng queueing behind a large chain-link fence.

"*Salam!*" I flash a wide grin. "What are you queueing for this time?"

"Not sure. We'll see when we get to the front," he winks, half-jokingly.

An elderly woman in a floral patterned *chador* spots me from the crowd as I pass her by. She grabs my arm assertively, but not unkindly.

"*Dokhtaram*, help us get through," she implores, eyes so tender it's almost heartbreaking.

There are times I fib to the security guards if I am walking in that direction and say that one or two of the people stuck behind the gate have to come in with me. Not that the guards always believe me or let them through. But sometimes, perhaps, we all pretend to look the other way, rebelling against the system. Unfortunately, today, I don't have time to be a rebel. I squeeze her hand apologetically, bow my head, and carry on walking straight ahead.

Just 20 metres farther, along the main road, stands a large tent structure known as Rubb Hall. It is where all the camp's newest arrivals are registered and placed until they are allocated a living space – most likely a meagre summer tent.

The structure is packed with hundreds of people – mostly Afghans, but also some Arabs, Congolese, Somalis, Cameroonians, Iranians and others, all squeezed into the confines of 200 square metres.

Some are lying down on tattered blankets on the cold, wooden floor, while others are crammed into grimy, dilapidated bunk beds, stacked like discarded relics in an overlooked attic.

I glimpse a group of young Afghan boys huddled in the near-right corner of the rectangular structure of Rubb Hall.

One of the Afghan boys in the group spots me from a distance and approaches; shyly at first, then confirming that I can speak his language, he lets his face break into a rugged, half-smile. Despite the unlit cigarette held tightly between his fingers, the pubertal acne dotting his complexion betrays his age to be no more than 14 or 15.

He searches my eyes for something – *anything* – that would give him some reassurance that he can really talk to me.

His eyes glimmer for a split second as he whips his police paper out of the front pocket of his denim trousers, unfolds it meticulously, then holds it out to me with trembling hands.

"Look, *khanoom* Maryam," he says, reading my name carefully off my badge. "They've made a huge mistake here."

I reach for the paper in his hand. My eye catches the miniature black and white photo of him on the left-hand side of the page, non-smiling, with his jet-black hair, staring back at me. In the photo, he appears to be standing in front of a metre tape which indicates his height to be 1.67 metres. His other details are recollected on the right-hand side of the page.

Last Name: RAMAZANI
First Name: MAHDI
Name of Father: MOHAMMAD REZA [*deceased*]
Name of Mother: AGHELA
Date of Birth: 01.01.2002
Citizenship: AFGHANISTAN
File: 7### - ##
D.K.A. 05/000######
Wanting Asylum: ---

Asylum: NO
Accommodation: MORIA

His date of arrival is stamped just below his details.

11/08/2018

It doesn't take me long to detect the mistake Mahdi is referring to. I have seen this before. During registration, when there are no official documents proving the person of concern's age, the registrars just hazard a guess about their date of birth, with no basis of factual evidence whatsoever. This is particularly a problem with unaccompanied minors. If their age is off by even a few months, they could be stripped of all protection rights that under 18s are entitled to – like safe shelter, the assignment of a legal guardian or discriminate access to food and non-food items.

Just as I predicted the boy to be no more than 15 before, had I been in a different position working in a different organisation, my estimation of his age could have turned into factual means of identification which could have changed this boy's life altogether. But I wasn't, and his registrar was apparently less fastidious.

"I am not 18," he exhales suddenly, trying to suppress the rage in his voice. "I told those idiots already. I am not 18." He scowls, then combs his fingers across his fringe, revealing a scar across his temple.

Before Mahdi has a chance to say more, another young man who was huddled in the corner with the other boys, this one perhaps five or six years older than Mahdi, walks towards me.

"I'd like to be younger too, Miss," he tells me with a smirk, punching Mahdi lightly in the arm. He holds out his paper in one hand, using his free hand to pull black baggy trousers up to his waist.

Last Name: QASSEMI
First Name: ABOLFAZL
Name of Father: ALI BABA
Name of Mother: YASAMIN
Date of Birth: 23.05.1999
Citizenship: AFGHANISTAN
File: 7### - ##
D.K.A. 05/000######
Wanting Asylum: ---
Asylum: NO
Accommodation: MORIA

"Abolfazl," I say his name contemplatively, then glance up at him for reassurance as to whether I have pronounced it correctly. But he doesn't meet my gaze. Instead, he stiffens at the sound of his own name. I feel insecure, not sure how I have wronged him, but certain that I have somehow unintentionally made him feel uncomfortable.

"It's Abe," he says sternly, in perfect English. "Call me Abe."

Before I have a chance to apologise, he shuffles away without another word.

I glance back at the young boy, Mahdi, who has not moved. He is flustered, agitated. He pulls a lighter out of his jeans' pocket and, with a shaky hand, lights the cigarette he seemed to have forgotten about. The smoke relaxes him a bit.

"I hope you can forgive my directness, *khanoom* Maryam," he begins, glancing back at my badge to make sure he remembers my name. "But I have faced more in my short life than perhaps you ever will. It is not that I can't handle it; I can take hardship."

He pauses for a moment, as if gripped by a memory. He holds his cigarette so expertly between his nimble fingers, like a connoisseur or an artist contemplating a masterpiece. The way he blows the smoke out of his mouth and nostrils at once makes him look years older and more experienced.

"But I thought it would end at some point, you know? That it would all lead somewhere; somewhere better." He turns his gaze back to me, quizzically searching my face with his dark, beady eyes, as if I can offer him something in return for his story. I can't, I am ashamed to admit.

"I am not 18," he keeps repeating, his eyes beseeching. "Please *khanoom Maryam*, tell them I am not 18." I shake my head. Telling 'them' would make no difference.

"You need to seek legal support," I explain, again knowing the chances of this making a real difference are also slim. Organisations offering legal support are so overrun on this island that dealing with age corrections will probably not be on their list of priorities. I stand quietly, apologetically, as I observe that initial glimmer of hope fade from his despondent eyes.

A slightly older man approaches me next. He is limping on a branch he is using as a makeshift walking stick – not because he is aged, but rather, it seems, because he has an injury on his left foot. Every time his heel grazes the floor, even slightly, his entire body flinches.

"*Dokhtar jan*, dear girl," he calls me, as he provocatively flicks Mahdi's paper away. Mahdi flares up at first, ready to fight back with the man, then seeing the imploring look in my eyes, decides to shuffle away instead.

The man waves his own paper in my face.

It never ceases to amaze me how new arrivals all seem so eager to show their police papers to anyone willing to take a look. The paper seems to give them some kind of legitimacy. Visibility, even.

Last Name: REZAEI
First Name: NAVID
Name of Father: ALIREZA
Name of Mother: MARIAM
Date of Birth: 27.09.1987
Citizenship: IRAN
File: 7### - ##
D.K.A. 05/000######
Wanting Asylum: ---
Asylum: NO
Accommodation: MORIA

Though the man is not much older than myself, grey streaks are already starting to gleam in his otherwise black, unkempt beard. His dark, shoulder-length hair is tied into a tight ponytail behind his head. The creases around his mouth mean he must have smiled once. Once, he may have been easy going, or made people laugh. But now, he stands before me in a crooked heap; like a hawk slowly starving to death, waiting for his prey to come out of its burrow.

"I have been in Rubb Hall for seven and a half months. Seven and a half months!" His voice breaks into a yell, loud enough for the tens of people around us to hear, but nNo one so much as blinks.

"They tried to house me in that caravan on the left side of

the slope, you know, the one in the corner with all the drug addicts?" He spits on the ground next to his walking stick.

"A bunch of useless men who just wait for the cash to come in every month to get high and get into senseless fights with each other – they are the ones causing trouble, but men like me are the ones who are paying for it! I told them, not in a million years would I accept to live with such filth. They keep saying there are no other free spaces in the camp. Liars!" He scoffs. "I can show you empty containers right now, but they say those are reserved for the new families. As if single men are not human. They think we are nothing!" He laughs as if he is choking. As if he has forgotten what laughter is meant for.

"I understand," I nod my head apologetically.

"And you, why are you here?" he asks, raising one eyebrow.

I tell him I am looking for the newcomers, particularly the women and children, because I work in a clinic with services tailored specifically to them. He lets out another half-hearted chuckle for the wrong reasons, as he begins to limp away, muttering almost to himself.

"You're all the same."

I swallow hard and shake off his sarcastic remark as best as I can; After all, getting used to passive aggressive comments comes with the job.

Next, I brace myself as I tread carefully towards a woman sitting cross-legged on a grey blanket in one corner of the First Reception Rubb Hall. A sky blue, cotton head scarf hangs loosely from her head, covering half of her auburn hair and shoulders. She is lost in thought, her eyes vacant, as she rocks her upper body gently from side to side, while cradling her police paper in her arms like a newborn baby.

"*Salam khanoom*. Are you new here?" I enquire, in a

somewhat rehearsed manner. She does not respond or even acknowledge me, but rather, murmurs something under her breath. I crouch down beside her, making sure to keep a fair distance to avoid making her feel crowded or uncomfortable. I wouldn't want a repetition of what happened with Abe.

"*Salam*," I say again, more softly. "My name is Maryam. What's yours?" Without lifting her gaze, she shoves her police paper in my face, as has become common practice among the newcomers. It is an act that says: *acknowledge me. Validate me. I have a name. I have a story.*

Last Name: HABIBZADA
First Name: ZARIFA
Name of Father: NASER ALI
Name of Mother: NAFISA
Date of Birth: 27.09.1987
Citizenship: AFGHANISTAN
File: 7### - ##
D.K.A. 05/000######
Wanting Asylum: ----
Asylum: NO
Accommodation: MORIA

1)KARIMI MILAD, son of MOHAMMAD ALI, born on 1/1/2006
2)KARIMI YAZNA, daughter of MOHAMMAD ALI, born on 1/1/2010
3)KARIMI AYLIN, daughter of MOHAMMAD ALI, born on 1/1/2017

"You have children?" I remark, as I glimpse her three dependents and their black and white pictures below hers. This time, she tilts her head up to look at me as she smiles wanly and nods. Before I can say another word, she lets her guard down and confesses,

"I never imagined my life would turn out like this. I was once top of my class, with prospects for a bright future. But everything changed when I got married."

She tells me her husband threatened to kill her and her son, so she had to take her children and make a run for it. She tells me she was robbed on her way over from Turkey; that she spent every single night praying and pleading to God just to let her survive until she could get Milad, Yazna and Aylin to safety. She tells me she thought people would be nice to her here. She shakes her head defeatedly as she says, "I was wrong."

I try to comfort her, convince her not to give up hope; I assure her that single mothers cannot be ignored for too long here.

"How long?" she asks, almost pleadingly.

I cannot answer that.

"A kind, old lady came to me on my first day here," she says with watery eyes. "Her black veil was wrapped so tightly around her head that I thought she was a woman of God, so I decided to trust her. She told me to go back and make up with my husband; she told me if I hurried, he might still forgive me for leaving him; that if I started the so-called *Voluntary Repatriation* procedure now, I might not have to wait so long. But I couldn't, I told the lady, because my husband threatened to kill my son, and now my son is very sick. And he needs to get to Athens as soon as possible to get proper treatment. There is no proper medical treatment on this island, you know?" She mentions it as a side note. I nod and gesture for her to continue.

"I asked the lady how long it would take to get out of this place. She looked at me so tenderly and then, out of nowhere, she laughed! It was a harsh, grazing kind of laughter. The kind that stays with you." Zarifa winces reflexively, as if she were fighting back the intrusive memory. "Not a minute ago, she had been this gentle, old woman offering me words of support. But then, she just laughed!"

"Sorry, *janam*," the old lady had told her at length. "It's just that, well, I can see you are new here."

Laughter has switched guises in this place. It has morphed into a disfigured version of itself, something that does not convey the happiness or exhilaration it is supposed to, but rather ridicule, bitterness and the most derisive kind of irony. The thought makes me shrink.

1.3 Zarifa

The sky gave me no warning. With its lovely shade of clear blue, and the sun glimmering in all its splendour, neither myself nor any of the other refugees whose tents are all splayed across *the Jungle* could really foresee the thunderstorm that awaited us during the night.

Back in Iran, all it took was one quick glance at the clouds overhead. If grey sheets were covering every inch of the sky, it meant a storm was in the making. I would call my son, Milad, to come running back home, wherever he was, to help me make our shelter waterproof before his father came back. The last thing we needed was to give my husband, Rahim, another excuse to take his anger out on me or the children.

God help us if there was ever a leak, even in the deepest corners of the kitchen where Rahim never even ventured. He would still somehow hear it, and I would most likely be the one to end up paying the price.

But that was in Iran. In Greece, storms like to come without notice.

After spending six sleepless nights on the hard, cold floor of Moria's First Reception Rubb Hall, amid heaps of other asylum seekers waiting to be housed somewhere – *anywhere* – a young American volunteer with long skirts finally approached me on the seventh day and asked for my police paper.

"Husband?" the volunteer enquired. I'd shaken my head matter-of-factly; the volunteer scribbled something down in her notes.

At length, the volunteer informed me that *sections D* and *E*, which are the designated safe areas for single mothers in the camp, were unfortunately packed with far too many residents already. She then gave me the option to wait patiently in Rubb Hall until something became available in the *sections* to which I gave an even more fervent shake of the head. –

"Take this tent and set it up wherever you find enough space," the volunteer sighed, in an almost apologetic tone – almost but not quite, because it is in her job description to be the bearer of bad news, so she must have been used to it by then.

To new residents like myself, setting up their tent *anywhere* meant in the sub-camp just beside Moria.

The Jungle, as it is known among refugees, or the *Olive Grove,* as the Europeans call it, is an immense area covering about 70.5k metres squared of rough, hilly terrain sloping ever upwards into vast expanses of fields. It is home to thousands of people from Afghanistan, and hundreds of others from Syria, Iraq, Palestine, Congo, Cameroon, Iran and so on. All of whom are probably being soaked through.

My little Aylin begins to whimper in her sleep when she hears the rainfall pattering against the tent's plastic cover, making her curl up closer to my bosom. But it is not until the leak in the tarpaulin gives way, and icy water begins to flood on to our exposed faces, that Aylin starts howling louder than the wind and shattering skies.

"Milad, *pesaram,* go out and fix the leak," I shout over the wind and the baby's cries. But my first-born cannot hear me. He stopped hearing me a long time ago.

He didn't use to be this absent in his earlier years. When God was kind enough to send Rahim away on his work trips, leaving me enough breathing room to be at ease with the children, those were the happiest days of our lives. Milad used to enjoy those fatherless days the most. He'd tell jokes and make Yazna tear up from laughing. He used to play with Aylin until she got tired and fell asleep on his lap. He used to eat whatever I cooked for dinner and asked for seconds. His eyes would sparkle every time he told me that, if he could have just one wish, it would be to move to Europe and become a famous footballer.

But ever since he had fallen ill, Milad was not that strong, playful boy I remember. It was about the same time he stopped going to his evening football matches. Whenever I asked why, he just shrugged his shoulders and busied himself with his phone. He barely ate, or showered, or spoke anymore.

My brother-in-law, Alisina, who had some self-proclaimed knowledge of internal medicine, had once suggested that it was probably a neurological disorder. Or maybe a psychological one. Perhaps even both.

"But what is certain, Zari *jan*, is that the boy is *irreparably damaged*."

This last bit, he whispered in hushed tones, lest the boy's father should hear and decide to throw him out onto the street right there and then. He'd once thrown a television set straight out of the open window because it had taken a few seconds too long to turn on. It was clear enough that Rahim had no patience for the *irreparably damaged*.

"There must be something we can do," I pleaded, my eyes welling up with tears. Alisina considered the question for a moment.

"You forget, Afghans are uninvited guests in this country. There is nothing you can do for him, at least not *here*."

My heart broke as I watched my son crouching in a corner of the tent, cradling his knees with his eyes firmly shut, trying to take deep, calming breaths as *kaka* Alisina had once instructed him to. Rainstorms like these brought back a tsunami of unforgettable memories from those rough nights in Iran.

I have no choice but to fix the leak myself. I peel off a frantic Aylin and hand her over to my older daughter. Yazna holds her little sister close to her chest and sways her from side to side, crooning for her to be quiet.

"*Tawakol be khoda*, I put my absolute faith in God," I mutter under my breath. Then, I wrap my *chador* tightly around my icy face and unzip the front of the tent.

It is raining so hard that I can barely see anything in front of me. My flip-flops sink into the muddy ground as I step outside to play the part of a handyman, not for the first time.

When I come back inside the tent, having succeeded in temporarily holding off the leak with one of my flip-flops, the children are huddled close together. As my eyes follow their chests, expanding then deflating with every breath, I swell up with sentiments of motherhood. The peace that my children find in their sleep is so unparalleled that it sometimes makes me wish they never wake up.

God forgive me. I don't mean it – not in that way, at least. But really, is that such a terrible thought? All I want is for my children to always have a chance to keep breathing freely. Just as they are right now.

When I come to lie down next to my children, my pelts grow heavy and the veins in my eyes pop, but my mind is so engaged that sleep does not find me. Instead, I stay fully alert until morning. Finally, when the sun's blinding rays seep through the tent's fabric, I blink my eyes open to the new day. The dampness of the tent has destroyed everything. The *naans* I purchased the day before for breakfast are now soggy. My grandmother's peacock blue shawl with gold sequins, that

I was planning to one day hand down to Yazna, is drenched and most likely ruined. Anything we managed to salvage that elicited any kind memories of our home in Mashhad is – to quote Alisina – *irreparably damaged*. The words send shivers down my spine every time I recall them. It's odd, how our memorabilia managed to survive the temperament of the sea, but not the wrath of the sky.

There is no point in idly lying down and mourning my losses, so I decide to get up and make myself useful. I grab a bar of soap and carefully hop over my sleeping angels and out of our tent into *the Jungle*. I collect our drenched clothes from the clothesline, shove them into a garbage bag, heave the bag up onto my shoulder and make my way down the muddy hill. I meander past the sleeping tents with difficulty, my squeaking sandals sinking into the sludge with every step, and wade my way onto the concrete slope. I trudge down past the military post, the *Safe Zone* shelter for unaccompanied minors, the impromptu fruit and vegetable merchants, and finally reach the toilet and shower containers.

They say that there is only one shower available for every 200 people in *the Jungle*, but even then, I have never seen a functioning one that was empty.

I unload the assortment of colourful clothes, that are now heavy with grimy rainwater, out of my bag and into one of the five wash basins next to the toilets and immerse myself into rewashing each item. It is not long before I spot a rather heavy middle-aged lady trudging towards the basins in her grey, plastic clogs. The strap has torn off on one side and is now gently whacking against her heel with every step. Massouma *khanoom* is dragging a large burlap sack behind her. Coming to a halt, she sets her sack down in the sink next to mine and takes a moment to adjust her white head scarf around her round face.

She opens her sack and fishes out her own bundle of damp clothes. The earthy smell makes my nose crinkle. I watch as my neighbour wrings out her garments and shakes off their dust, before submerging them under the icy tap water that makes her large hands quiver.

"*Salam Alaykum*, Massouma *khanoom*," I greet my friend indulgently. "Welcome, welcome dear. Did the rain get you last night too?"

"*Ya Allah*! It's all soaked," Massouma croaks. Though her voice is usually gruff in its natural state, it appears even more hoarse now that she is struggling to speak over her sore throat. "Can you believe it? I had just washed everything!"

Massouma *khanoom* is a conservative woman in her fifties. She arrived in Moria at around the same time as me, with her son and daughter, both adolescents, and her much older husband. He barely manages to wake himself up in the mornings, let alone help his wife and children with any of the household chores or errands.

We have some things in common, Massouma *khanoom* and I. She is not unfamiliar with receiving the occasional beating from her husband every time she complains about his lack of support. But unlike myself, Massouma believes no matter how useless a husband is, it is a wife's solemn duty to put up with him until the end of his days. So, instead of leaving him, she prefers to let him be and secretly wishes he dies of a stroke in his sleep.

"Hand me the soap, please, Zarifa *jan*," Massouma *khanoom* wheezes in between coughs.

I rub the bar of soap on the black leggings I have in my grip a few more times before passing it over to Massouma *khanoom*.

"You should really see a doctor about that cough, sister," I advise her.

"The doctors here are a joke! You stand in line for hours, and then they tell you to drink water, and you'll be fine. That is their solution for everything, just drink water!" Massouma retorts scornfully. "You could drop dead before their eyes, and they would still tell you to drink water!"

"Will you look at that?" I say reproachfully, staring up at the bright blue sky overhead. I cup my hand over my eyes to shield my face from the sun's rays. "It's as if the sky doesn't even care that it almost drowned us last night!"

"*Sobh bekhair*, good morning!" Kareema's voice sings out, as it usually does before she is even within earshot. Kareema is sporting her denim trousers, pink flip-flops and red flannel shirt, while cradling a pile of dirty plates and cups in her arms. How she manages to look so stylish at all times of the day and night is puzzling. I sometimes wonder whether she simply wakes up this way.

"What a nice day today; may it remain this way," Kareema coos enthusiastically as she draws closer.

"May God hear your words," Massouma and I both echo.

"Why don't you wash your clothes over at the *playground*?" Kareema asks, perplexed by the bunches of dirty laundry occupying the wash basins. "They have ten washing machines over there now."

"More lines? Sister, please," Massouma *khanoom* grunts again. "I waited in line for hours last Thursday morning, and for what? To be told that they ran out of tickets! It's the same story every single time. I will do my laundry by hand, thank you very much." She scours one garment against another vigorously in an attempt to remove a stubborn mud stain.

"My grandmother always said, God rest her soul," I second Massouma's remark, "that if we were to wash our dirty clothes with machines, then why did God give us these two hands?"

"It's true. You see these?" Massouma flashes her pruny hands triumphantly, as if holding up ancient heirlooms. She traces the lines, creases and wrinkles on one palm with her finger; perhaps a few too many for a woman in her mid-40s. "These are the result of years of scrubbing. Clothes, shoes, bags, dolls, dishes – you name it, they've scrubbed it!"

"Suit yourself," Kareema shrugs, as she takes up another empty sink.

She flicks back the end of her designer headscarf and begins to soak her plates in cold water and suds. Kareema is in her late 30s. She lives a few tents away from us with her husband Amir and their two sons, Mirfaiz and Abbas, aged 14 and 11. Other than the fact that she has a talent for looking glamorous from dawn until dusk, and probably even beyond that, the other feature that sets Kareema apart from other women in *the Jungle* is that she has a flair for gossip. She is always the first to hear fresh news about any of the residents, camp workers or organisations – like the bit about the new washing machines. Let it be known that we women heard it from Kareema first. But how she is always the first to learn these things, or who she learns them from, is yet another mystery none of us can solve.

"How is your son, Zarifa *jan*? Mirfaiz and Abbas keep asking when he will come to play football with them and the other boys."

I shift my weight from one leg to the other, averting her gaze. It pains me when people refer to my son so casually, as if they have the slightest idea what is wrong with him or what he has been through.

"Soon, *inshAllah*," I say simply.

"*Madar jan*," Massouma's 15-year-old daughter, Samira, suddenly scampers towards the sinks.

I am more than grateful for the interruption. Samira is donning some baggy denim trousers, a pair of worn trainers and an oversized beige shirt, which is clearly more suited to her mother's figure. I cannot help but smile to myself as I spot the girl hurriedly poking her loose curls back under her navy-blue veil before her mother tells her off for not wearing it properly.

"*Madar jan*, can I have some money?"

Massouma *khanoom* lifts her gaze from the sink, slowly scrutinising her daughter from head to toe, and scowls.

"First of all, where is your *salam*?" she scolds. "I swear these kids nowadays don't know the first thing about manners!"

"Sorry, *madar jan*. Salam, hello, ladies. How do you do?"

"*Alayke salam*, Samira, dear. If you are fine, then we are fine," I respond. Kareema seconds with a cheerful nod.

The girl waits, twiddling her thumbs and fingers, but Massouma *khanoom* just continues washing some Bermuda shorts, a garment completely at odds with the increasingly cold weather. It is probably the only thing left over from the donation drives last month.

"*Madar jan*..." Samira begins again, tentatively.

"Yes, I heard you," her mother cuts her off. "What does a girl your age need money for?"

"There are these gorgeous bracelets, only €3.50, *madar jan*! All my friends—"

"All your friends, all your friends. HA! You hear that, Zarifa *jan*? Kids nowadays have no decency. Maybe you should worry less about your friends and come and help your poor, old mother. Go on, grab your own dirty clothes and start scrubbing."

Samira heaves a deep sigh, sags over to the sink and does as she is told.

Kareema finishes washing her plates, shakes out the water on them, then stacks them on top of each other.

"By the way, did you hear about Freba *khanoom*'s daughter, Parwana?" she brings her voice down to a whisper and smacks her strawberry-glossed lips together as she pauses.

"What about her? Did something happen?" Massouma *khanoom*, Samira and I sing out in a chorus.

Kareema wiggles her eyebrows, then rotates and squares her hips towards us, like a world-class magician about to unveil how she performs her tricks.

"Well, it was past midnight, and Parwana had to use the loo. I keep telling her not to drink all that *chai* at night, but you know that girl never listens! And the poor dear tried so very hard to hold it, but after a while, she just had to give in and go. She kept saying to herself that it would be alright, that there wouldn't be any queues, and that she would be back in ten minutes. So, she shoved her blankets aside, soundlessly stepped over her sleeping husband, trying her best not to stir him, unzipped the mouth of the tent as quietly as she could and trod out into the stormy night.

"You all remember where their tent is, right? In the very heart of *the Jungle*, a few tents across from the Heydari family's. So, the poor girl made her way through the mudslides in the dark, curbed the string mesh nets circling the tents and shanties, stooped down under the clotheslines, and in all that rush, she even forgot to put on her headscarf! And all the while with the rain pounding down on her. Can you imagine?"

"May God forgive her!" mutters Massouma *khanoom* under her breath, fishing out the tawny prayer beads from under her cardigan and pressing them tightly against her massive bosom.

"So anyway, she finally made it to one of these toilet containers here – God knows which one – and shut the door behind her. But the poor girl had been so intent on relieving herself that it wasn't until the very last minute when she suddenly–" Kareema pauses dramatically, tucking her chin in like a turtle withdrawing into its shell.

The three of us lean in closer.

"When she suddenly what?"

"How can I put it?" Kareema considers. "Well, she suddenly realised she was knee-deep in a mountain of – God forgive me – in a mountain of manure!"

"EWWWW!" We all let out in an ensemble. Even Kareema herself, who is the one recounting the story, cannot help scrunching up her face as she reveals her plot twist.

"Oh, God, have mercy on us!" I exclaim, slapping my right palm on the back of my left hand. "This camp is the end of our dignity."

"Why did she even go all the way there?" Samira chimes in. "Just go in the field, for God's sake!"

"Bite your tongue, Samira; you should never go in the field!" her mother chastises her. "What if there are men watching?"

"I would rather take my chances with the peeping men than the shit mountain!" Samira lets out, before she can contain herself.

"Language, Samira!" her mother exclaims, slapping her across the back of her head. Samira hangs her head down low and says no more.

"Did you hear that noise last Friday night?" I weigh in. "I was so scared!"

"The drunk men had another fight. I heard someone got

stabbed!" Kareema says shakily. "And my boy, Mirfaiz, had not come home yet. I thought maybe he had been injured! *Khoda rahm kone*, may God have mercy!"

"*Wallah*, I never let my daughter go out after six. It's not safe! Isn't that right, Samira?" Massouma nudges Samira, whose form is now perched meekly over the wash basin. She wrings the water out of the shirt she has just hand-washed and moans in agreement without lifting her head up.

"Someone gets stabbed every night; get used to it, *azizam*. *Salam* ladies," Roya strides towards us slowly, dirty dishes in one hand while resting the other on her bulging belly. She occupies the basin on the far-right corner and busies herself with rinsing her dirty dishes.

"Don't say that! You will bring bad omens." Massouma clutches her prayer beads again, weaving them between her index finger and thumb.

"Bad omens are already upon those who live in *the Jungle*, *khala jan*," Roya retorts.

I still remember when Roya and her husband, Arsalan, first arrived in Moria, over five months ago. They were young, hopeful newlyweds, and no one could tell from her slight belly bump that she was 14 weeks pregnant. Now, wherever she goes, her belly precedes her, as if it were testing the grounds and letting her know the coast is clear for her dramatic entrance. Being eight months pregnant and still carrying out daily tasks such as cleaning, washing and standing for hours in the food line might be considered admirable for some, but for the residents of Moria and *the Jungle*, it is more than commonplace.

"You need to rest more in your condition, Roya *jan*," Kareema says gently, waving a finger at the bags under Roya's eyes.

"Sleep?" Roya chuckles, not unkindly. "What sleep? That

word has tasted bitter ever since my husband and I got here. If it is not the rain, it is the neighbours' shouting. If it's not the shouting, it's the drunken idiots loitering outside our tent. If it's not that, it is the rumblings of hunger left by the inedible food here. How can anyone sleep in this place?"

"I know what you mean. Abbas's appetite is so meagre that he has lost five kilos in these three months," Karima remarks, her eyes wide with a mother's worry. "And every time I take him to the doctor, they just send me away because, according to them, it is not an emergency." Her rising pitch betrays hints of disappointment and anger all at once.

"Don't bother – they'll just tell him to drink water!" Massouma snaps, her eyebrows twisting into a frown.

"It was so cold last night. So, so cold," Roya reflects, her voice barely rising above a murmur. "I keep thinking, how can I ever bring my newborn baby up in this place? I told Arsalan, if he expects me to give birth here, he should just kill me right now."

My eyes fill to the brim with tears for this young, soon-to-be mother, and as I glance around, I see all the other women are also holding back tears of their own. All of them except for Roya herself, who is most likely so tired of crying that she probably doesn't have any more tears left to shed.

"Moria is a woman's hell," she finally says, almost as an afterthought.

I contemplate her words, recalling all the difficult moments I have been made to live through in Iran, Turkey and on the way here, and whether it comes even close to bringing my children up in this limbo. Not knowing whether we will stay or be deported, nor how long we will have to live in tents, in this weather. Not knowing is the worst state.

For some time, nothing can be heard but the splashing of water and clanking of dishes. Kareema waits for Roya to finish shaking her plates dry, then the two of them bid us a good day and make their way back to their tents. Massouma *khanoom*, Samira and I squeeze the last drops of clear water out of our laundry in stony silence, then stuff our damp clothes back into our bags.

The sky above us begins to turn a hint of grey and breaks into light a drizzle. My face is wet within seconds, but this time, not from tears. Disappointed though I am, at least this time I am grateful that the sky has bothered to give me a warning.

"Same time tomorrow?" I ask, with a hint of bitter irony in my voice.

"If the pneumonia doesn't kill me first," Massouma wheezes, pulling the hem of her cardigan over her head. "*Yallah*, Samira. Let's go."

1.4 Abe

Abe is not my real name, but it is the name I would much rather have. I like names that leave something to the imagination – where I am from, what I do, who I am. I hate the kind of names that instantly give away the whole history of a nation when uttered. I have always blamed my parents for not having chosen a less Afghan name for me.

Calling me by my real name, like Maryam *khanoom* did the other day, sends chills down my spine. It brings back memories of a life I'd rather forget.

Unlike most of my friends, who proudly parade our country's flag in the form of armbands, wristbands or even tattoos, I have never really counted myself as a patriot. I came to Europe to forget about Afghanistan and everything associated with it. I don't celebrate *Nowrooz* or fast during the month of *Ramadan* anymore. I exclusively listen to American and European rap music. I don't even speak Dari unless I absolutely have to.

All of the Hazara people I know in this camp hate it when they are mistaken for being from China, Korea, Japan, Malaysia or any other number of East Asian countries. They puff out their chests smugly and say to their confused interlocutors, "No, my friend, we are from Afghanistan." Unlike most Afghans, I am not keen for Europeans to believe they know everything I represent just by looking into my eyes.

When I was a boy growing up in Ghazni, I used to love playing football. I was very good at it, but my cousin wasn't, and he was always jealous of me because of that. So once, when we were playing, he set up a trap for me. He planted a big rock right in the middle of the field and tipped all the other kids off about it except for me, knowing that I would be so focused on the ball that I wouldn't notice it. I tripped over the rock, the sharp edges caught the fabric of my trousers and they ripped. I bled, and the other boys laughed.

I ran home, red-faced, clinging to the waist of my trousers as best as I could and, once I got there, I pulled them off and handed them straight to my mother. She immediately reached out for her thread and needle, which she always kept at hand's length, and began to sew the rip back together. She didn't ask me what had happened. She knew that if there was something on my mind, I would tell her.

"Didn't you ever think that with a name like Abolfazl I would be chained to this backward country for the rest of my life?" I sputtered reproachfully. My mother just shook her head and laughed, like she always did whenever we discussed anything that made her feel uncomfortable.

After Afghanistan, we moved to Iran, where I was told at the age of 12 that I was too old to go to school. They thought we were worthless – so much so that we didn't even have a right to an education. And as time went by, their mentality started to meld with my own and take a toll on my life. I kept thinking to myself that if I had just been born to Iranian parents, I would be entitled to a normal life, with access to school, college, and decent work and pay.

I learned to hate Afghanistan and everything it stood for. I made a vow that the day I stepped foot onto European soil, I would get as far away from everything that reminded me of the wretched country and never look back.

That was the plan, at least. Until I met her.

Shahgul.

It means the king of all flowers. It is as if God himself

has had a hand in naming her. Maybe it is the fact that I see something familiar in the gleam of her honey-coloured eyes that does not make me want to run away. Or how I feel myself dissolving into the ground every time the sun's rays bounce off her sun-kissed complexion. Or maybe it is the way she pronounces Dari words in her soft, Herati lilt that makes me taste sweet, warm milk with cardamom every time she speaks.

She is a few years older than me, and she is not alone either. She has a daughter, Frishta, who is like a miniature version of her mother – so strong and wise beyond her years – and a son, my little man, Mohsen, whose eyes always brighten up like flashing bulbs whenever he hears my voice.

Every morning, before sunrise, Shahgul comes to my tent with the children and murmurs my name softly from outside, so as not to rouse my roommates.

"Abolfazl."

"My name is Abe," I say half-grouchily, half in jest, as I step out to meet them.

"No, it's Abolfazl," she always responds teasingly, sticking the tip of her tongue out in that way that sends my heart fluttering. And then the four of us go to *Zone 10* of *the Jungle* together to help the other bakers make *naan* while Mohsen plays with the other children.

Naan is Shahgul's craft, passed down from relatives who used to have a chain of bakeries in Herat. The way she massages and kneads the dough with her dexterous hands; it is like watching an artist spin clay into pottery.

Frishta, being her mother's daughter, is very good at it too. She is an artist at heart. My dough, on the other hand, usually ends up clotted and lumpy, and I have to rely on Shahgul's long, nimble fingers to bail me out. And she always does with a sweet, gentle grin.

Somehow, the three of them have made me see the good in being Afghan, and the things I once felt ashamed of are beginning to lose meaning. They remind me of the days I was happy in my country because the truth is, those days did exist, as much as I have tried to block them out. Like the days of indiscriminate learning with the other boys in the *maktab*. Or those days I spent observing my mother skillfully stitch pretty much anything thrown in her direction back together, even tattered rags or shreds of cloth. I have even begun to like the sound of the name my parents gave me.

* * * * *

When my eyes open to flashes of sunlight seeping through my tent, I feel suddenly giddy. I reach out for my phone to confirm what the sun's high position in the sky has already given away. The time is 08:17 AM. By some miracle, I am awake before Shahgul and the kids.

I hop to my feet and begin to groom my defiant, shaggy hair with a comb. Hamed and Navid are still fast asleep, squeezed together in the corner of the tent, but that is nothing new – they often sleep late into the afternoon. Single men are notorious in Moria for getting drunk at night and sleeping it off the next day, recharging for another night of drowning their sorrows. Not to say these guys are the trouble-making kind, but they do indulge in the occasional drink or three; why not admit it?

The only other person awake is our mysterious roommate, Gul Agha – a quiet, middle-aged man who often hides behind his thick glasses with his head buried in his phone, furiously typing away to God-knows-who. But that is no surprise. The other guys and I have started to question whether he ever sleeps at all.

"*Sobh bekhair,* Gul Agha," I whisper hoarsely.

He lifts his eyes for a second to indulge me with a nod, then goes back to his typing.

After I pull on my hoodie and the socks I'd left out to dry, I check the time on my phone again: 08:45 AM. Shahgul has never been this late. The bakers must already be almost done preparing the morning's dough.

Something feels wrong. As I listen closer, I begin to hear what sounds like large crowds not too far away from my tent. There is also an odd smell in the air, something that reminds me of burned toast or brimstone.

My heart begins to pound against my chest. I swiftly unzip the tent, step outside and suddenly, all my senses are under attack. My eyes water; my mouth tastes bitter; even my nostrils scorch. Tendrils of black smoke cover the sky above Moria.

It isn't long before my roommates are outside, standing next to me.

"What's going on?" Hamed asks, still too groggy to make sense of the fact that Moria is on fire.

Someone else says something, but all I can hear now is my heart drumming against my chest and throat all at once. My voice dries up, and my lips refuse to pry open to produce a response. I squint up at the sky and, with my blurry vision, somehow manage to glimpse the source of the smoke. The caravan across from the food line, next to the power grid.

That's right next to Shahgul's caravan.

I try to swallow the iron fist in my throat and, without thinking, start to run towards the smoke. Someone tugs my arm – at least I think they do – trying to hold me back, but I shake myself free and sprint at full velocity.

Before I reach the food line, something crackles, and

one of the caravans erupts. Glass shatters, pieces of worn metal fly off in all directions and the screaming masses of refugees around the food line begin to sprint haphazardly. It is the caravan with the graffiti of the choir children singing. I remember the day some Dutch volunteers enlisted the help of the Afghan kids in the camp in painting that piece. Frishta was so excited; the girl loves to paint.

My eyes water again, this time with tears, burning my skin as they trickle down my face. I shut them so hard that they sting. Dark circles begin to dance under my lids as I wish the nightmare away with all my heart.

When I open them again, the flames have turned a blazing orange and obscure grey and are now rising high into the sky. My chest tightens; my veins constrict as oxygen ceases to reach my vital organs. Every heartbeat sends jolts of pain pulsating through my entire body. The fire spreads its tentacles to the next caravan, beginning to devour it whole. Above all the clamour, a woman's scream punctures the air.

It's her.

Shahgul.

1.5 Frishta

The camp is burning!

I don't know how it happened. All I know is that everyone is crying and screaming and running like mad people, especially the adults. My head hurts.

The moment I smelled the smoke, I ran out of our caravan. I am in the middle of hundreds, maybe thousands of people. Where is Mummy?

I can hear her screaming my name.

"Frishta! Frishta!" She seems lost. *Frishta* means angel in Dari. Mummy says my birth was a gift from heaven, so that is why she named me Frishta.

"Frishta, where are you?" she cries out for me over the crowd.

I can see her now. She looks so sad when she is worried. She has been sad ever since we arrived in Moria, and I don't know what to do to help her. Sometimes, when she thinks me and my brother are asleep, she sobs quietly to herself. She thinks I don't hear her, but I do. I know she feels lonely sometimes. I was still very small when *baba* passed away – may God rest his soul. Mummy has had to raise us without much support.

At least back in Herat, she had my aunties and grandpa and grandma to help out sometimes. But when bad people attacked our village, we had no choice but to leave. Here, we have no family to help us. So, she cries sometimes, and I hear her. I want to tell her not to worry; I want to tell her that she is not alone, that I am with her. I want to tell her I am not a little girl anymore. I am grown up and I can pull my weight too.

"Frishta!"

"I am here, Mummy. It's okay; I am safe!" I yell back, but she can't hear me. She just keeps turning on her heels in circles, stretching up on her tiptoes, trying to see over the crowds.

I spot *kaka* Abolfazl as he finds her. He is also shaking, but calms down when he sees she is okay. Then he says something which seems to relax her a bit too. He must have told her I'd made it out and not to worry. He is so nice, *kaka* Abolfazl. Sometimes, when Mummy is too busy to go to the food line, he shares some of his own food with us. He does act a bit young when he is with his friends, but when it comes to us and Mummy, he is so caring and mature. Mohsen really likes him too, because he can just sit and play with him for hours. I wish *kaka* Abolfazl was my father and he would always stay to help Mummy and play with Mohsen.

Mohsen is my little brother. He is five, but Mummy still treats him like a baby. When I was five, I was already helping Mummy clean the house and wash our clothes. Once, when Mummy was nursing Mohsen back to sleep after one of his usual nightmares about the bad men who attacked our village, I asked her who she loved more: me or Mohsen. She waved me away casually.

"Don't ask silly questions, Frishta. I am not in the mood."

Now she calls Mohsen's name. That is when I notice he is not there with Mummy. It is strange not to see him by Mummy's side. They are usually inseparable. Even when I want to hold Mummy's hand, he always gets to her first. And I get angry at him sometimes, but Mummy tuts and says I am older, so I should be patient.

Selfish, thoughtless Mohsen! It is just like him to go missing at such a moment and worry Mummy.

She is beginning to panic; I can see it in her shaking body, and to be honest, so am I. He may be annoying sometimes, but he is still my little brother.

"Where are you, Mohsen?"

I stop to look around and see no sign of him. He is usually so loud that you can't help but notice him, even over hundreds of screaming people. My heart stops beating when I remember the last place I saw him: in our caravan. We go to sleep at the same time, but he always falls asleep before me, and I watch him as he does, just to make sure he is breathing okay. What if he is still in there?

The flames are getting bigger now, and I can see them approaching our caravan. I see Mummy looking in the same direction; then, as realisation dawns on her, she starts pushing and shoving people out of her way like a mad woman. People hold her back.

"It is too dangerous," they say. "He will be gone by the time you get there," they say. "You will kill yourself."

Mummy is frantic. I have never seen her like this. We are all she has, Mohsen and me. And I can't let her lose him like she did *baba*. So I brace myself and dash through gaps between the crowds and back up the slope before anyone can stop me. I dive into the smoke.

There is too much commotion. I feel like I am in a haze. In seconds, my throat and nostrils are in pain, my eyes begin to tear and smoke enters my lungs. I pull the hem of my shirt up to cover my nostrils, but I have already breathed in too much of it, so it is not long before my body begins to crunch. I am coughing in fits.

I hold my breath and enter our caravan through its unhinged door. Beyond the thick smoke, I spot him, doubled over in the corner. Poor, little Mohsen. He is crying so hard but stops for a moment when he spots me.

Hang on, little brother. I am coming for you!

Making my way to the corner of the caravan is harder than I thought. It is so hot, worse than the summers in Afghanistan.

I am sweating like crazy, and every inhale feels like needles poking at my chest. But somehow, I jump over the wreckage and carefully brush past the growing blaze. Then, I crouch down on my hands and knees and take Mohsen into my arms. That makes him relax a bit.

All of a sudden, there is a yellow spill of light and the loudest sound I have ever heard, like something rumbling and shattering and blowing up all at once. On instinct, I shield Mohsen as best as I can, with my body half-covering his. And then I am in a daze. I can't hear or see anything. Time slows down as I try to blink.

There is a searing pain in my right eye, like it has been pricked with something sharp. I peer down at Mohsen through my left eye. He is still clinging onto me for dear life. I think he is wailing, but I still can't hear properly. I squint back to see the shattered window of the caravan, with hundreds, maybe thousands, of shards of broken glass on the floor. That must be what that sound was. The flame is burning bigger and brighter than ever, inching closer, threatening to eat us alive. *Ay Khuda*, it is so incredibly hot!

It takes me a few more seconds to realise I need to move, but I am rooted into the ground, shaking and light-headed, gasping for air. My hearing begins to return, but the vision on my right side is still blurry. I have no choice but to act now, even if it means relying on my left eye only to see where I am going. I scoop my screaming brother onto my back, pull the hem of my shirt back tightly over my nose and jolt out of the door of the caravan. I run as fast as my legs can manage, with Mohsen's weight spread unevenly across my shoulders, in the opposite direction of the smoke.

Fire engines are arriving. Men with uniforms are yelling at

everyone to clear the camp's exit. I stagger to the gates, which are now thrown wide open to make way for the trucks.

I am covered head to toe in ash and soot. I see Mummy and *kaka* Abolfazl standing in the first row of the crowd. *Kaka* Abolfazl is holding Mummy up, who looks weaker and paler than ever, as if all the blood has been drained from her face. She looks like she is having trouble standing up. Did she faint while I was gone?

When she sees me and Mohsen, she jerks back to life. I hand over my crying brother to *kaka* Abolfazl, who instantly scoops him up into his arms and carries him away from the mess, leaving me with Mummy. I am dizzy and tired and just want to collapse into her arms. But I don't. Instead, I try to be strong for her.

Mummy drops to her knees, lifts my chin with one hand and cups my cheek with the other, letting out a deep sigh of relief. She immediately runs her fingers over my face, examining it, looking for wounds or burns.

She stops short and gasps at the sight of my bad eye. I still can't see too well, but at least it doesn't hurt so much anymore. That is, until Mummy lightly brushes my pelt with one finger, sending a singeing pain through the entire right side of my face and down to my throat. I wish I could contain it, but I can't, so I wince. I can tell by Mummy's sudden change of expression that it is serious. Then, out of nowhere, she draws her hand back and slaps me squarely across my left cheek. It burns hotter than the fire.

She is weeping uncontrollably now as she pulls me in for a tight hug.

I didn't mean to make you cry, Mummy. I was just trying to help. I thought if you saw what I am capable of, then you would stop crying yourself to sleep every night.

She pulls away again and braces herself, but I linger for

a bit, wishing we could hug forever. She lifts herself off her knees and wipes her eyes with her headscarf, revealing her beautiful face. But it is not the face I just saw a few minutes ago when I found her in crowd leaning on *kaka* Abolfazl. And it is also not the face I have been seeing every night since we came here, when she thinks I can't see her.

She may have been lost for a while, gone to a place from which there would be no return. But now, something in her expression has changed. Her eyes are bright and warm like fire. She is back to her old self; the strong Mummy I knew, who used to laugh despite the hardship. The strong Mummy who started working two jobs the day after *baba* died, just to feed and clothe us. The strong Mummy who stood up to the bad man who tried to leave us for dead in the jungles of Turkey.

That is the Mummy I have been missing all these months. But she is back now. She is strong. And she loves me more than anything; I can feel it.

"Come on," she says, beginning to remember how to smile again, as she reaches her hand out to hold mine. "Let's go and find an abandoned tent in *the Jungle* and set up shelter for tonight."

1.6 Maryam

"Right, this is it," says the clinic manager. She's a butch blond woman in her mid-30s, who is tattooed all over. "There has been a fire in the camp, so casualties are expected. Remember your mass casualty training, people?"

Without waiting for a reply, she claps her hands together.

"Positions, everyone."

The team disperses like ammo, taking up their pre-assigned posts at the gate, the triage table and the different tents designated for either green, yellow or red categories of patients. Given my lack of medical background, I am asked to oversee the green tent.

"Remember, green means go," our trainer, a meek man with a French accent, said, adjusting his thin-framed glasses over his beaky nose. He had flown in from Brussels in the morning to train the local clinic staff and planned to leave that same afternoon, figuring it should not take too long.

"Assign patients with a non-emergency status to the green tent," he continued. "Keep them under observation for 20-30 minutes, then let them go."

* * * * *

My role in the clinic is hazy in mass casualty situations. Though on a regular day, I would be in charge of promoting health education and community engagement; in emergencies, I am often most useful as a counselling aid-slash-crowd controller. My Farsi and French language skills also always come in handy if we happen to be short on interpreters, which we always are.

It is odd to see the rectangular tent we usually use for our educational sessions turned into a rudimentary doctor's surgery. The two long benches facing each other at each side of the tent now serve as makeshift beds for patients, should they need them. The small office at the back is to be used for the psychological first aid sessions that we are expecting. Fire always triggers the resurfacing of traumas that people are trying hard to bury.

The tent is large enough for up to 10-15 patients, if need be. But at the moment, there is no one in sight.

We bide our time for what feels like hours, just waiting. And *waiting. And waiting.*

The nurse, a young Greek graduate in her early 20s, keeps shuffling through the medication box and taking inventory, as if something is bound to be missing.

The psychologist, also a Greek girl but in her late 20s, is flipping through her notes in a more composed manner, dog-earing the pages she thinks might be of use when the inflow of patients begins to arrive.

I can never stay still in these situations. I keep popping my head out of the tent to get a view of the gate.

As nerve-wracking as it all is, I almost wish the patients would start arriving already. Anything has to be better than all this waiting around.

"Anyone?" I call out to Yusif.

"Nothing," he sighs wearily.

Yusif is a tall Syrian man in his late 20s who once lived in Moria camp himself. The incident has shaken him more than any of us, though his face would not tell you as much.

He is pacing back and forth along the gate, with his head dropped low. All this waiting around must be eating him alive too. He is much more of an adrenaline junkie than the rest of us here, always the first to get wind of these situations and always the first one on site when there is an incident in the camp.

"How do you always get here before the rest of us, Yusif?"

He lifts his head and holds my gaze for a moment.

"I'm redeeming myself," he says, with a wan smile.

"For what?" I venture.

"It should be me on the other side of that gate."

He drops his head back down and continues pacing.

Guilt is a big criterion in humanitarian workers' job descriptions. For one reason or another, to succeed in the field, you somehow have to feel like you haven't suffered enough to get there.

Faint screams from a distance shake me by the shoulders.

The sky is dark, so I can't see much, but the screams are drawing nearer to the gate. A woman. Crying, like she has just lost the best part of herself.

Shadows move into view, and with the dim lights around the clinic, I finally see her face: a middle-aged woman with a blue headscarf and disoriented eyes. Two men are holding her up by the arms and helping to guide her towards the clinic. Yusif pulls the heavy gates open immediately and they hurry through.

"What happened?" I ask the younger man, who must be the woman's son.

"She got scared of the flames and started screaming," he says between pants.

"My sister died in a fire some years ago – it must have triggered something."

I rush them to the triage nurse, who starts registering their information.

Before long, the woman is identified as Zahra Hossaini, is diagnosed as a green patient who is having a panic attack, and is sent to our tent.

Her son and the older man, who must have been her husband, are to stay in the waiting area while Zahra *khanoom* is treated.

By the time she is sitting on one of our benches, she has stopped screaming, but she is still dazed. She fixes her vacant gaze on one corner of the wooden structure holding up the tent.

"How are you feeling?" I try asking her – or, what is left of her.

Her expression is hollow, as if her soul has left her body. If she is thinking of anything at all, it is nothing tangible, and certainly nothing to do with the present moment.

I decide to let her rest for a few minutes before trying to speak to her again.

"My name is Maryam. I am here if you need anything."

She still doesn't respond. Instead, she begins to sob quietly to herself. I take her ice-cold hand in mine, trying to offer her some warmth.

"It's going to be okay," I say soothingly, as she lets the side of her head drop onto my shoulder. "Your son and husband are just outside. Would you like to see them?"

She shakes her head, then wipes away her tears with the tip of her scarf.

At least she can hear me now; that's a good sign. I wave the psychologist over, who then leads Zahra *khanoom* to the small space behind at the back of the tent, where they sit down for a proper consultation behind a closed door.

Before long, the clinic is full of patients – a few scorched by the flames, a few injured while scrambling to make their way out of their burning tents or caravans. But the majority of the patients are here due to some other ailments that our clinic treat on a daily basis: children with diarrhoea or skin rashes, and other illnesses that are all too common for Moria. Thankfully, the fire didn't do much damage this time.

While Zahra *khanoom* is still in her consultation with the psychologist, I hear another woman's screams and rush out to the gate. A mother is sprinting towards me, carrying an unconscious boy, no older than four, in her arms. Yusif unbolts the gate to let her in and she rushes past us, straight to the triage nurse, with no need for a guide.

The nurse, knowing the boy's condition only too well, grabs him from the mother's arms and carries him straight to the red zone, where severe cases are treated. The mother is instructed to stay in the waiting area. She is frantic and crying, swaying back and forth, as if she is naked without her son in her arms. I sit her down on a bench next to me.

"*Chi shode?* What's happened?" I ask, calmly.

"My boy," she says between sobs. "He is epileptic. He has more episodes when he is ill or has a fever. The doctors in Afghanistan said if he continues to have these episodes, he will be brain damaged before long."

Her lips quiver as she speaks, sending a quake all over her body. I put my arm around her shoulder. The trembling dies down slightly, but she is still weeping.

"You did well in bringing him here. He is with the doctor now, and he will be okay. You'll see."

A little while later, the triage nurse steps in to tell the woman the boy is conscious now, but has to be kept under observation for another half an hour. That seems to make her relax. Just then, a man steps into the waiting area and rushes over to where we are sitting.

"Is he okay?" he asks the woman hurriedly, face pale.

"He will be fine," I say with a smile. I stand up and let the woman's husband take my place next to her.

"*Tashakur*," he utters. His voice is rough and gravelly, like he hasn't gotten a wink of sleep for the past few nights. I nod, before making my way back to the green tent.

The door to the back office opens, and Zahra *khanoom* is led out by the psychologist's arm. She has started crying again, so they are taking her to the doctor for a sedative.

"What's wrong with her?" asks another woman, who is sitting on the bench, cradling her baby as Zahra *khanoom* walks past us.

"The fire has shaken her up."

"The fire," the woman muses, as if something suddenly clicks into place.

"I'd forgotten all about it," she chortles dejectedly, pressing her baby closer to her bosom.

STAGE 2: ANGER

When the first stage of denial cannot be maintained any longer, it is replaced by feelings of anger, rage, envy and resentment. The logical next question becomes: "Why me?" [...] Maybe we too would be angry if all our life activities were interrupted so prematurely [...] What else would we do with our anger but let it out on the people who are most likely to enjoy all these things? People who rush busily around only to remind us that we cannot even stand on our two feet anymore [...] People who tell us to lie still [...] when we feel like jumping out of our skin to be doing something in order to know we are still functioning on some level! [...]
So this patient makes sure that he is not forgotten. He will raise his voice, he will make demands, he will complain and ask to be given attention, perhaps as the last loud cry, "I am alive, don't forget that. You can hear my voice, I am not dead yet!"³

Elisabeth Kübler-Ross

---

3   Kubler-Ross, Elisabeth. On Death and Dying: What the Dying Have to Teach Doctors, Nurses, Clergy and Their Own Families. Scribner, 2014.

2.1 Abe

Minutes have turned into hours; hours into days; days into weeks. Today might be Monday or Tuesday, or perhaps even Wednesday. I might be sitting in my tent with my back to the guys, or I might be aimlessly shuffling through the camp's roads and alleys, just one more among hundreds of wandering refugees. My movements have become mechanical and plaintive. I might be getting in line for breakfast, lunch or dinner. It doesn't matter which.

It's been 13 days since the fire broke out in the camp, and every day since, it is becoming more obvious that they think our lives are expendable. No great material damage was done – just a few tents and caravans were wrecked and hastily replaced within a few days. Good as new, according to the authorities. When it comes to keeping us contained, they certainly know how to act fast.

But what they have been keeping covered up is that a life was lost. A five-year-old Afghan boy called Yaser Niyazi, who was fast asleep at the time his caravan caught fire. His parents were out running errands. They figured it would only take them a few hours and that they'd be back by the time Yaser woke up. How could they have guessed something as trivial as leaving the heater on would kill their only son?

The real cause of the boy's death is the negligence of European authorities. They turn a blind eye to 20,000 people who have no choice but to plug into the same power source, causing deadly circuit overloads.

I went to see Yaser's parents the other day. The father just sits slouched forward, with his head buried in his burly hands.

And the mother – oh, the poor woman. Every time she tries to formulate words, they get stuck in her throat, as if they were scraping together like pieces of broken glass.

If you were to ask the camp's authorities, though, none of this ever happened. There never was a boy named Yaser, and Mr and Mrs Niyazi must just be traumatised – *quite understandably so* – by the dreadful event of the fire itself; perhaps it triggered some memories of past events. The world will never know about Yaser. His name will be buried among thousands of other children who get caught up in the crossfire of their parents' useless dreams of escaping war and poverty.

When I think of Yaser, I can't help but also think of Frishta and Mohsen. Their caravan was the next one to catch fire after Yaser's and, had it not been for the fact that Frishta went back to rescue her little brother – and God's mercy that helped them make it out in one piece – they would not be here today either. Their names would be buried along with Yaser's, and Shahgul would be dismissed as another frantic, childless woman who traumatises easily.

After many pleas and protests from equally outraged refugees, the authorities have finally decided to call a general meeting. Community representatives have been invited to pose their questions directly to the camp's administrators. I have been selected to attend on behalf of the Afghans. They say that because I speak good English, I should represent them in these kinds of meetings from now on. I don't know about that, but when I heard the camp manager would be there, I was eager to attend for myself, just to give him a piece of my mind.

I sit in a circle with six other men representing their own communities from Syria, Congo, Cameroon, Somalia and two other African countries. The circle is completed by a bunch of arrogant military men in their 40s and 50s, shutting down our concerns as soon as they are raised. Clearly, they have more pressing matters on their mind than trying to appease the likes of us.

I bite my lip while the other representatives nod complacently as each of their questions about the cause of the fire, and how to avoid such incidents in the future, are quickly dismissed. It is becoming clear as day that the reason behind this meeting is to save face.

As the military men grunt and try to hurry our questions along, an image of Shahgul flickers into my mind. The way she quavered with grief when she thought Mohsen and Frishta were dead. The way the blood drained from her face and how her feet gave way; the way she collapsed into my arms, and for a moment, made me feel like everything was lost.

At the end of the meeting, the camp manager – a veteran in his 60s with a husky, arrogant voice and steel eyes – asks if anyone has any other business. The wrath in the pit of my stomach, the one I have been keeping in check for all these days, begins to wake up – like a minute blue flame gradually fanned into a raging red blaze. The kind of blaze that killed a five-year boy and just as easily swept his ashes into oblivion. The kind of blaze that could even scorch a 60-year-old former military man, no matter how tough he thinks he is.

I stand up from my chair in one swift motion and, without thinking, pick it up and throw it against the wall behind me. All heads turn towards me. The room falls dead silent. Rage seethes in my faltering voice and trembling hands.

"How many of my people have to die until you treat us like human beings?"

The camp manager raises an eyebrow. I have finally thrown him off guard. He glares at me through suspicious eyes for an instant then, without another word, clears his throat and dismisses me from the meeting. When I refuse to move, he swiftly signals for his police henchmen to escort me out of the room. Two of them grab me by the arms, but I shake myself free and steal out of the room myself, slamming the door behind me.

Later, I receive several congratulatory pats on the back from the other representatives and members of the community for standing up to the *devil*. But I don't feel any lighter or more appeased. Raising my voice in a contained meeting won't bring back the dead. Neither will it prevent future deaths or make this camp any more bearable for the thousands who are expected to live here, day by day, not knowing whether they will live to see another morning.

There has to be something else we can do to get some attention. Something that lets people all over the country and all over Europe, even, know what is really going on behind the barbed wire fences and concrete walls of this camp. Something that leaves a mark; something that singes them just as they have got used to letting us burn.

By the end of the day, I am pure heat. And I cannot wait to unleash.

2.2 Zarifa

The day is teeming with warmth and sunlight, with a clear blue sky and flickers of sunshine gleaming overhead. Never mind that we are in the middle of autumn. Even the sun in Moria has become unbearable lately. I used to think of sunshine as a gift from God. Not here. Here, the rays perforate my skin. It doesn't really matter whether I am out and exposed or safely tucked away in my tent. Somehow, the sun always manages to find me and burn me.

Right now, I am standing patiently in the women's line for the second time today, ready to spare countless more hours waiting, fidgeting and perspiring while sandwiched between hundreds of other bodies, queueing for food handouts. My head is throbbing and hot under my crimson scarf. It is as if its thick fabric is absorbing every last ray of sun from the stifling air and pumping it into my brain. Nevertheless, my eyes are alert. They dart back and forth, scanning the surroundings, briefly retaining the weary faces of the other refugee women congregated next to the familiar metal bars leading up to the camp's kitchen.

The sound of growling stomachs fills the lazy air. The aroma of raw chicken and boiled rice makes me feel both famished as a reflex and, at the same time, it makes the skin on my back crawl. My senses are at war with each other. One part of my brain deceives me by triggering the memory of what decent food, like *ghorme sabzi*, used to smell like back home, and tries to equate the odour with that. The other part of my brain simply struggles to warn me about the implications of feeding myself and my children this garbage they call food in order to survive. We don't have money to keep buying meals from the

Afghan bazaar all the time either, so this will have to do.

It is not the queueing in Moria that is the problem. In fact, I think I am starting to get used to spending hours of my day standing in line. It gives me some time to think. The real problem is that I could wait for hours, compressed between sweltering bodies; my guts twisting and wrenching in hunger, my feet aching, then reach the front of the line and still end up with nothing. I could wait for hours just to end up observing that indifferent look on the faces of the kitchen staff as they shrug their shoulders as if to say *sorry, you will have to go hungry tonight. Again.* That's what has been happening in the past two weeks at least, since the number of arrivals was *unexpectedly* high, leaving the kitchen short-handed.

An immense woman in black tilts her head back slightly. We lock eyes for a moment. The woman's *abaya* and even the expression on her pudgy face are mournful. Other than her punctuality and the fact that she is an Arab, I know little about her. But I can tell from her demeanour, the way she carries herself and purses her lips when concentrating on an unmoving point in the distance, that she was more than just a refugee once. But now she is just one more among thousands of women relying on charity and handouts to survive.

Moria is an equaliser in that it makes everyone, no matter what lives they lived in the past or what baggage they carry with them into the present, into no one.

Something about the woman's gaze reminds me of my old psychology professor, the time before my right to a higher education was seized away by the father of my children.

It was not easy for an Afghan to attend university in Iran, but I had insisted that my studies were my life, and my family had found a way to make it happen. I would pull all-nighters and study more than all of my peers with the hope of achieving top grades and coming first in my class. And I did, every single semester, come first. Education was my weapon, and I was determined to learn to yield it, to defend my dream of one day making a difference.

That was before I got married. It was not exactly a forced marriage, but my family was knee-deep in debt, and his family had promised to pay it all off in return for a subservient bride. At first, he'd been kind, supportive and a great provider. Everything, in fact, a woman at an economic disadvantage like me could have hoped for. He had made me believe it was precisely my burning passion to make a difference in the world that had made him fall in love with me. He had told me he would stand by me every step of the way. But then, everything changed. The moment we said our vows, the moment we stepped out into the world as newlyweds, the fairy tale I'd begun to entertain as the man of my life vanished. Instead, he was replaced by an abusive, hateful monster. Like a darkness that had been lurking somewhere deep down inside him had been unleashed the moment we became husband and wife. I never understood why.

He started by forbidding me from attending college study groups and get-togethers, saying that was no place for a married woman. Then, he started pulling me out of class because, according to him, they were affecting my daily chores. And one day, he called the university to declare I was dropping out permanently. Every time I tried to speak up, he'd beat me. Then, he would go out, get drunk, get high, come back home and beat me again.

I prayed to God every night for it to stop. I asked for guidance, but none came. I even considered asking for help, but I didn't know how. Then came the children: first Milad, then Yazna and then little Aylin. The three of them were the light of my eyes. So, I stayed – for them. And I never uttered a word. Instead, I took the beatings without a tear; I bruised silently; and I withered internally.

One day, he beat me loudly, kicking me in the ribs while I was lying half-unconscious on the floor. That was when my son, Milad, ran into the room and yelled for him to stop. And he did, for a moment, stop. I thought that might be the breakthrough he had been lacking all this time. But instead, he mustered up all his force and kicked my son in the chest so hard that he was thrust into the back wall. I wanted to run to him, kneel beside him, shield him with my entire being, but I was in so much pain. I lay on my stomach, facing the wall, eyes bloodshot, listening to Milad gasping for air. I heard my husband approach him and my son begin to hyperventilate.

What is he doing to him? That monster!

I wanted to scream out for the whole world to hear, but the excruciating pain kept me silent.

Finally, my husband made his way towards the door. Before leaving, he yelled the words that changed everything.

"If you ever interfere in my business again, I will make sure you breathe your last breath. Understand, boy?"

That was the moment when I made my decision. I would leave him, and I would save my children from the darkness.

* * * * *

Just to the left of the women's line, there is a steel, chain-link perimeter, erected like a cage. It holds thousands of men, propped up shoulder to shoulder, hip to hip, also queueing for food. The army keeps the men's line separate from the women's, since past incidents of poking and groping, and then screaming and crying.

As more and more men are herded into the line, it isn't long before the space becomes tighter and more claustrophobic.

There is a sudden eruption of hollers. Cries. Threats. Indistinguishable words in Dari and Arabic are hurled across the crowds of men. Someone has cut in line. Another has shoved someone else; and another has placed his hand where it should not have been. The men are about to throw down, like caged animals pawing for scraps.

Fight. Fight. Fight.

The crowds are getting riled up. But before anything happens, one of the crowd controllers, a tall, lanky man with beady eyes and an air of self-importance, steps in between them. The fight dissipates before it has a chance to start.

Crowd controllers are just volunteers from the camp. They are refugees themselves, but when they don their badges, they transform into hawks. They bide their time, leering at the herds of men from the very front of the line and weed out the weak from the strong.

I glance away from the men's line, glad I am nowhere near that hot mess. Though things are not always calm in the women's line either. It would be careless for me to ever let my guard down here, so I make it a point to always be fully aware of the women immediately ahead and behind me, just in case I have to defend my children's right to eat.

All around me, I see familiar but emaciated faces, dreary from the nights of sleeplessness and days of hunger, edging steadily forward in line like the walking dead. An absence of energy might make some turn listless, but what it does to the majority of the women in Moria is, instead, to cultivate their survival instincts. It is as if we have all made a vow to abandon the skins of our former lives and step into the wild, ready to pounce and tear each other to shreds should the need arise.

The Qur'an says God sees everything.

"Whether you conceal what is in your hearts or disclose it, Allah knows it. Allah knows what is in the heavens and in the earth and He has power over everything."

And yet in this place, we all somehow stop fearing Allah or the day of judgement, and just pray every night for his long-overdue protection.

* * * * *

In my evolutionary psychology class at college, I had an argument with my professor about the physiological impact of the acute stress response, or what is more commonly known as the fight or flight mode.

World renowned physiologist, Walter Cannon, discovered that the human body's sympathetic nervous system is activated when faced with perceived danger, leading to the sudden release of hormones from the adrenal glands, like a deer, grazing on the green, faced by a hungry lion. Since deer do not stand a chance against predators, once their survival instinct kicks in, they have no choice but to flee. But if it were another animal, like a chimpanzee facing off with a hungry lion, perhaps he could grab a hold of a rock or a dead branch nearby and fight his way to survival.

"What about those who would neither fight nor flee?" I had asked my professor.

He assured me with compassionate eyes. "There are no such people or animals."

"But what about the ones who would just rather lie down and die?"

* * * * *

Something is wrong. The queue has not moved an inch in the past hour. I crane my head, trying to get a look at the front of the line, but suddenly stop short when I catch a glimpse of a skeleton of a woman with a ramshackle frame appearing right next to me. Her pea green Lycra head scarf is fitted so closely around her face that it makes her look like a snake. Where did she come from? She had not been there a minute ago, I am sure of it. But something about her face looks familiar.

The woman presses her lips together, then smiles, flashing her sunken cheekbones, as if they had been carved into marble. Then, out of nowhere, the woman throws her head back and laughs. And that is when I recognise her. The old woman from Rubb Hall. The one I'd chosen to trust on my first day in the camp; the one who had cruelly laughed in my face when I had poured my heart out and confided in her.

Her sadistic laughter has left a permanent mark, making me want to dig a ditch and climb inside to conceal myself from the face of the Earth every time it echoes in my mind.

I size the vile woman up. I can take her on if I have to. After all, I have the element of surprise on my side. No one expects someone as gentle and meek as myself to be such a strategist. Just as I am about to dismiss the woman as harmless, she is the one to surprise me by throwing a piercing look in my direction. Then, out of nowhere, the woman snarls through gritted teeth.

I stay still, composed. The next move is not mine. The woman nudges me with her elbow, trying to cut in front of me, with no apology in her countenance. She grabs my arm and tries to shove me aside.

The battle for sustenance is about to begin. I am ready to obliterate anyone who stands in my way, even a fragile, old thing, like this witch.

My heart begins to race, and my breathing turns into a cadenced panting. Fight or flight mode activated. With one sweep of the arm, I thrust the woman away. Then, I brace myself for the impending violence that will follow.

Like an animal. Like a savage.

Like I had not once been a woman of God or a young college student with aspirations to make the world a better place through education. Like that person is dead now, and her replacement has been thrown into a pit with a piece of bread hanging over her head and told to wrestle for it, with hundreds of others, to see who emerges as a victor. Like an invisible Caesar is keeping watch over us here in Moria, pulling at the inconspicuous strings attached to our shoulder blades and biceps as we dance for them, letting it all happen in hope of just making it to the next day.

The woman and I stare each other down. The crowds of women in the line begin to step aside, making way for the fight that is about to ensue. I pull my shoulders back and root my feet into the ground, steadying my pose. The enemy flashes her clenched teeth, never once faltering. My muscles tense. I am ready to swoop. The enemy's complexion pales; her pupils dilate. My heart pounds against my chest. The enemy's grips tighten into fists. Our eyes lock: mine fierce; hers taunting.

"Your move, *khanoom*," I breathe.

Again, the woman throws her head back and cackles in her revolting way. Then, she casually shuffles away, waving a dismissive hand in the air. She has made her choice; she has chosen to flee.

It seems my college professor was right. When it comes to survival, people either fight or flee; there is no room for resignation. It seems I've turned out to be the fighting type. So, I need to keep my guard up. No fight today. But there is always tomorrow.

2.3 Frishta

It's so early, the sun isn't even up yet. We're sitting on a bench in the cold, alongside many other mummies and daddies, just outside of the asylum services office. Mummy looks so pretty with her shade of pink lipstick, her eyelids painted bright blue and the edges of her white veil, lifting with the wind like butterfly wings.

But she is nervous. I can tell because she keeps rubbing her hands together, almost as if she is trying to get out a stain.

Mohsen stayed behind with *kaka* Abolfazl, but I insisted on tagging along. I rarely leave Mummy's sight since the fire. This way, she knows I am always safe. But least of all today. I know what an important day this is for her. For all of us, really. The day we have been waiting for and scared of at the same time. The day that, according to Mummy and *kaka* Abolfazl, *will map out our future*. Today is the day of our interview. Even thinking about the word *interview* makes my tummy hurt.

I suddenly feel like reaching for Mummy's hand and taking it into mine. She squeezes my hand to comfort me in return, trying her best to calm her nerves. The steel door of the office opens with a thud, and a young Afghan boy, who must be the interpreter or *tarjoman,* pokes his head out. The *tarjoman* has black hair and is carrying a bunch of papers under his arm.

"*Khanoome* Ghafori?" he calls out, looking around in the crowd.

"Here."

Mummy stands up and drags me to my feet. The man peeks down at me with a queer look on his face, then up at Mummy. I suppose it has something to do with the fact that children are not usually allowed to take part in asylum interviews.

"Please, she won't be any bother," Mummy pleads.

The man's eyes dart back down to me, still unsure. I flash the widest, sweetest grin I can muster and watch as he melts. That's my superpower: my smile. And I'm not afraid to use it.

"Alright then," he says, giving me a quick smile in return before he steps aside, leaving the way open for us to enter the room.

It is a small, dim room with no windows, and mostly empty, aside from the large, white table right in the middle of it, which makes the room look even smaller. A Greek lady is glued to her chair on the other side of the table. I can't see much of her face as her nose is buried in a bunch of papers. All I can see is her oily, black hair tied back into a plait.

Mr *tarjoman* joins the lady on the other side of the table and whispers something in her ear. She nods. Without lifting her head, the woman points to the steel chairs next to the door and we sit. She reaches her hand out to Mummy, and Mummy presents her with her threefold *Ausweis* paper, the one we got after the police paper. The lady takes it out of her hand and fills out her details on a new sheet of paper. Then, for the first time since we stepped into the room, the lady speaks.

"Why are you here?"

She doesn't waste any time. The indifference in her voice makes me feel weak in the knees. I can tell she has been asking the same question hundreds of times and is not interested in the hundreds of answers she must receive every day. That's not a good start for us.

But Mummy is calm. She has rehearsed this part, so she takes a deep breath in and begins to tell her story.

"Our village in Herat was attacked. I had no choice but to get my children to safety and—"

The woman holds her hand up in a stop sign.

"Tell me about your husband," she commands.

Mr *tarjoman* translates the question into Dari. Mummy hesitates. Her eyes twitch. She is starting to panic. This question, she was not expecting.

"Gone," she says faintly.

Mummy never speaks about *baba*'s death. Every time I try to ask her about him, all she does is cough and try to change the subject.

"Dead?" The lady asks coldly. This time, she sounds curious. I see a sudden curve in her mouth. *Is she enjoying this?*

I glance over at Mummy, and she is biting her bottom lip. She's afraid. Terrified.

Surely *baba* would come up at some point, she must have known that much, but maybe not this early on in the conversation. Something is holding her back. Like she is afraid the truth won't be good enough for this woman.

She is suddenly twitching again, pulling at her sleeves, rubbing her hands together. She averts the woman's eyes, and instead turns to look at me. I nod as if to say, *go on. Just tell them, Mummy.*

"No," she exhales suddenly. "I don't know where he is."

I feel my heart stop beating in my chest. My throat is dry. I can't close my mouth. I don't understand. Everybody said he died when I was too young to remember. Why would they lie? Or is it that she is lying right now?

"He left years ago. It was an arranged marriage. I never knew him or his family. One day, he just walked out of the door and never came back. Years later, someone from the village told me he had remarried and had another family in Pakistan. That's all I know."

My face is frozen. I can't move my body. I try to picture him. What he might have looked like. What he might have said when he left. Did he ever try to call or write? Did he know where we were now? Did he care?

Mummy has tears in her eyes. She turns her head around again to look at me and, seeing the shock in my face, she breaks down and cries so loudly it breaks my heart.

Mr *tarjoman* is shifting in his chair, probably wanting to offer some words of comfort. He is waiting for a cue from the lady. But nothing comes from her. No comforting words, no *would you like to take a break?* She has not even bothered to glance up since we sat down.

Instead, she scribbles furiously on her paper and asks matter-of-factly, "Is that all?"

The sound of her casual voice makes me hold onto the edge of my seat so hard my fingers turn white. There is so much pain in my tummy, the kind that makes me either want to shout and scream at the world or burst into tears.

For a second, something breaks open inside me. Maybe it is that we are just one more case to this lady. Maybe it is that our lives mean nothing to her. Or maybe I want to look into her eyes so badly, just once, to see if they are really made of steel. I throw myself off the chair and scream at the top of my lungs, "*Say kon!* Look what you did to my mother!"

For the first time since we came in, the woman lifts her head and purses her lips. As I thought, her eyes are lifeless. She asks the *tarjoman* for a translation. He mutters hurriedly and her eyebrow shoots up like a fishhook. She glares at me in a way that makes me feel suddenly cold. But I am not scared of her.

"Monster!" I yell, standing my ground.

"That's enough, Fristha," Mummy tries to say, but her voice catches in her throat.

The woman says something in Greek to the *tarjoman*. He

sighs heavily and rises to his feet.

"Come with me," he tells me.

I glance at Mummy with sad eyes, but she nods sternly. I follow the *tarjoman* out of the room.

I wait outside for what might be another hour, twirling my thumbs and fingers. There is a lot of noise outside of the gates. Refugees are gathering in large groups, yelling and shouting loud enough for the oily lady and her colleagues to hear, making the kinds of demands no one ever listens to.

The door finally opens and Mummy steps back out. Her eyes are red and puffy, as if she has not slept in weeks. She kneels down beside me and grabs me by the shoulders. I cringe suddenly as she raises a hand, thinking she might slap me for my outburst. But instead, she gingerly brushes my hair away from my forehead.

"I was trying to protect you," she says, her eyes twinkling with tears again. "I'm sorry."

I shake my head. *I know*, I want to tell her. *It's okay*. But I can't speak because something is making my throat sting. I have tears behind my eyes, but I will not cry. Mummy dabs at my eyes with the edges of her headscarf. She smiles, that kind smile that sends an instant warm feeling through my heart, as if to say everything is going to be okay. And I feel calm again.

2.4 Maryam

Crowds are gathering outside the gates of the asylum services in the camp. 20 or maybe 30 women on one side, 40 or 50 men on the other. And then, there are the minors. Unsure of themselves, yet still ready to prove their courage to the world. This is their chance to prove they are men, not boys.

Another day, another protest. It won't be long before it is quashed. The camp manager has got used to keeping the riot police at hand's length, always on standby.

Between the tens of bare faces and draping hijabs, I spot Zarifa in the crowd, holding baby Aylin in her arms.

"Salam Zarifa *jan*," I wave, as I squeeze through the throng. "What's going on?"

"Salam Maryam *jan*," she shouts over the clamour. "You know, same as ever. Demand this, demand that. Stay until dinnertime, get nothing in return. Apply. Rinse. Repeat," she says, sighing.

Aylin is wriggling in her arms, trying to break free from her mother's embrace.

"Sit still, *azizam*," she rebukes, repositioning the baby, before turning her gaze back to me. "And what brings you to the camp today?"

"Oh, I was just looking for one of our patients who has an appointment with the midwife," I say, casually pulling the appointment card out of my vest's pocket. "But I gather with all this going on, she won't be easy to find."Just then, Zarifa waves over a large lady, weaving her way through the crowd.

"Massouma *khanoom*, over here. Welcome, sister."

The heavy, imposing woman shoves her way through the clamour and usurps a spot right next to Zarifa, a disgruntled expression on her red, puffy face. The day's heat must not sit too well with her.

"Salam *alaykum*, Zarifa *jan*," she says in her hoarse voice.

"*Alayke Salam*, Massouma *khanoom*."

Zarifa glances back at me.

"Do you know each other?"

The large lady grunts dismissively.

"*Koshbakhtam*, Massouma *khanoom*. Nice to meet you." I bow my head, with one hand over my heart, as people in my country do to show respect when greeting elders. "My name is Maryam. I work in the clinic across the road."

"I know your *clinic*," she hisses, emphasising the last word as if it were anything but that. "What kind of a *clinic* refuses to see my teenage daughter, Samira, who has been coughing her guts out for the past two weeks? Huh? Tell me, if that's what you call a clinic."

I'm taken aback, but not surprised. Dealing with disenchanted patients or in this case, refused patients, is part of my role.

"I'm sorry to hear that," I say in low tones. "And I understand your frustration. But a lot of times, our clinic has the capacity to offer emergency care only."

The woman is simmering now. I have unwittingly unleashed something in her. Rage is surfacing in bright red blotches all over her face. She raises her voice loud enough for the other refugees around to hear.

"Do we have to bring in a dead body before you choose to help us?"

A throng of supporters begin to gather behind the woman, echoing her anger and mumbling in agreement. I shift my gaze towards Zarifa, who lowers her head, as if to utter a wordless apology on her friend's behalf.

My gaze shifts back to Massouma.

"*Khanoom*, please try to understand," I try to keep my voice from shaking. "It is not that we don't want to help you. It is that we don't have enough staff, enough time, or enough space to tend to everyone. And there are cases that take priority because they are, medically speaking, more urgent."

"Then pack up and leave!" The lady barks at everyone and anyone who is willing to listen. Her voice is so hoarse now, it might tear up her throat. "If you can't handle everyone in this camp, then bring us a clinic that can."

"Hear, hear," cheer her throng of supporters.

I bristle. My heart is racing. Resistance groups are forming and, where once their target may have been the camp and broken asylum system at whose mercy they live by, now their anger is redirected at me. A pawn in a much larger game of humanitarian support. And this, when my defences are at their lowest.

An adolescent boy steps out from between the crowd. I recognise him immediately from his jet-black hair and the scar on his temple. *Mahdi.*

"Leave her alone, she is just a *tarjoman*. It's not *her* fault." He tilts his head to peer at me for a moment.

I choose not to correct his statement about me being just an interpreter; I don't see how it would help the situation. Instead, I offer Mahdi a distracted smile.

He nods complacently and turns back to the crowd again.

"It's that there is no system here. This camp and everything around it has been intentionally built to silence us."

His speech throws me for a moment. For a boy his age, he seems to have more understanding than many of the much older adults gathered around him.

"Oh, please. She is just like the rest of them," the older woman groans, shooting me a dark look.

That remark again. I have heard it too many times since I started wearing this vest and donning this badge. And though every time it hurts, I can usually keep my anger in check. But this time, for some reason, being equated to systems and organisations that thrive on human suffering pulls the trigger for me. Something tells me not to let it slide. Not this time.

Adrenaline thrums through my body, making my muscles tense. I feel suddenly revived, shedding my cloak of diplomacy – my fear, my empathy, all of it – down a drain along with my vest with its flashing red logo. And despite all instinct to stay calm, a rage is seething in the pit of my stomach that cannot go unchecked.

As a humanitarian worker, I am instructed to stay calm in the face of an ambush. But as an imperfect human being, I can't help but raise up my shield. When you feel pinned to a corner and squeezed by the throat, you have no choice but to try and thwart the attack.

"How dare you?" I hiss back through gritted teeth. This throws Massouma off slightly. Her vicious look warps into one of perplexity. "You have no idea who I am," I continue, unfazed. "You have no idea what I gave up to be here."

She composes herself again.

"Then leave!" she yells back, spewing the words out in an exasperated rush. "You think we want to be here? You think we wouldn't leave this hell if we could? If you can go, then go! *Yallah*, leave us be. It is not like you are doing us any favours."

I feel like I have been slapped squarely in the face. Punched in the stomach. Like all the air has suddenly left my lungs in a rush. Something wells in my throat, and I struggle to hold back the tears. But I can't. So, I let myself cry. Despite all efforts to stay professional, in front of the entire world, I let myself cry. Mixed expressions of victory, anger and pity scrutinise me. I feel naked; like a wounded gazelle with no fight or flight left in her, sprawled on the ground, ready to be torn to shreds by a pride of lions.

Minutes later, I feel a hand on my shoulder. I turn back to see Yusif standing right behind me, looking at me with an air of concern. He must have seen the whole thing. The yelling. The outburst. And now, the tears rolling shamelessly down my cheeks.

"Are you okay?" Yusif asks in his most gentle voice.

No, I am not okay. I feel hazy, like I am not myself. Like I haven't been myself for a long time. Like I don't even know who I am anymore, or what I am doing in this camp. I feel unhinged and vulnerable, wearing my heart on my sleeve when I am more than certain that it has no right to be there.

I shake my head.

"I don't know."

The throng begins to disperse, moving towards the camp's exit, suddenly remembering I am not their main target after all. Zarifa is gone. So is Mahdi. Massouma is plonking away as well, without even giving me another look.

Yusif tugs on my arm compassionately now, trying to bring me back.

"Come on. Let's get out of here."

I nod, follow him out of the camp and back to the clinic, where I plan to hide out for the rest of my shift.

2.5 Mahdi

02:27 PM: Refugees have started to assemble outside the camp's perimeter. Finally. We were supposed to gather here at 02:00 PM, but seeing as how everything in this country is always delayed, we have started to live our lives accordingly.

Men, women and children. Afghan, Arab, Iranian, African. We are all in it together. Some of them look pale; you can tell it is their first time in a gathering of this size. Others are more composed, but still not undetermined. Others still are flustered, annoyed – infuriated, even. Anything could set them off. Those are the ones to look out for. The ticking time bombs who usually take things too far in protests. We are still trying to go for a peaceful protest at this point. But I have no idea if we can keep to that. So why deny it? The truth is that it might turn into a riot.

It was Abe, the new community representative. He started this protest, and I was one of the first to jump on board. Why? Because I'm tired. I'm tired of the administration's excuses when I keep telling them my real age. I'm tired of living hand to mouth in Rubb Hall, filled with hundreds of noisy, stinky people, with nothing but a blanket to keep me warm in the freezing nights. I'm tired of living at the mercy of racist laws and inhumane regulations.

So, when I saw my chance, I took it. I was the one who rallied up the other boys in Rubb Hall, outside the gates of the asylum services. I followed Abe's lead as he yelled out demands that meant something to all of the people trapped in this hell of a camp. Food. Shelter. Safety. Dignity. We played on their frustrations and fanned their flames. And then, once we got them really riled up, Abe suggested we take it to the streets.

There is a meadow next to my house in Dasht-e Archi, that smells like orange blossoms and freshly baked bread. Baba stays at the mosque to eat with the men, and madar jan takes me and my two younger sisters, Sara and Somaya, there for picnics every Friday after Jummah prayers. She strums an old sitar my grandfather had left her and hums the melody to an old folk song entirely out of tune. To my childish ears, though, it is beautiful and, for years, I think that is what the song is actually supposed to sound like.

After a light lunch of naan, eggs and potatoes, Sara and I play this stupid kids' game. Sara places her palms beneath mine, grazing them lightly, then when I least expect it, she slaps me over the back of my hands. If I am not quick enough to draw my hands back, she wins. And she often does win.

When it is my turn to do the hand slapping, I strike Sara's hands so hard she ends up crying. And my mother suddenly stops playing her music, scowls at me and, with that, I know it is time to go home. I am about six or seven years old.

03:37 PM: The crowds have got bigger than I thought. Abe is up front, trying to keep the crowds moving in an almost orderly fashion. Navid is limping up behind him, trying to keep up as best as he can. Even having a bad leg is not enough to stop him from joining in this protest. And look, there's that cute girl who lives in the *Jungle*, Samira, in the middle of the crowd with her huge mother, along with everyone else. It is almost thrilling to see everybody banding together for what feels like the first time.

We pump our fists in the air, our expressions resolute, as we form a moving procession. There is so much adrenaline pulsing through my veins, I haven't even had the urge to smoke today. Chants of *"Azady"* puncture the thick air, even from those who do not speak our language. Freedom, that's all we want, that is all *I* have ever wanted. Hundreds of protesters march side by side from the camp's entrance towards the town of Mytilini, which is about eight kilometres away, crying out loud enough for the whole world to hear, demanding our freedom.

I am eight when I witness my first execution. The stench of sweat and blood combine to make my stomach churn and my head spin. I could not have imagined it would be so easy to kill a person. The assassin is a boy himself, no more than 15 or 16, when he is instructed by his superiors to pull the trigger. He does it without a moment's hesitation. As if God himself bid him to kill the innocent man.

The man tumbles to the floor, eyes no longer pleading, mouth no longer in the shape of a lower-case "o", muttering duas *under his breath. The woman, his wife, bawls in the corner while pulling her children in a tight, almost painful embrace to shield them from the sight of their father, lying in a pool of his own blood. One child, a mischievous boy, pulls away and uncovers his eyes.*

The boy looks from his father to the assassin. Something about his gaze makes the killer uneasy, so he makes a sudden movement and loses balance, dropping his rifle at the boy's feet. The boy picks up the weapon and examines it. Something about brushing his finger along its grip makes all his fears melt away and he casually points the muzzle at his father's killer.

The killer raises his head off the floor and trembles. In war, it is often the case that the prey becomes the predator, and the hunter becomes the hunted.

04:07 PM: They have closed off the roads to cars and other vehicles. We have been marching for more than an hour and are now reaching Kara Tepe refugee camp, which is about 4 km to the southwest of Moria, halfway to the town's centre. Mothers hold their children's hands and fathers follow closely behind as they exit Kara Tepe camp. They stare at us, the chanting throng, in astonishment.

I am not sure what the refugees in this camp did to deserve a better life than the rest of us. No tents in this camp, only caravans. Much more space and classes to sign up for as well. But for them to let you into this camp, you have to be sick or disabled or something. Though most of the people I see here look and sound healthier than I have ever felt in my life.

We call out to the refugees at the gate of Kara Tepe camp, beckoning for them to join the movement. Some of them do, while others turn on their heels and retreat back into their caravans.

04:32 PM: Slightly further down, squads of armed men in khaki uniforms, helmets and shields form a line right in front of the gas station to block our access to town. Something about so many armed men seems too familiar. Suddenly, my temple stings. I rub at it frantically with my fingers in an attempt to assuage the invasion of the past.

I am 12 when half a dozen men in uniform rap on our door, almost breaking it down in one swift blow. Now the man of the house, I instruct my mother to huddle in the corner with my two younger sisters while I answer. It is me they are after.

One of the men points a rifle in my face, so close I can feel the cold steel on the tip of my nose. Fight for us or die. Those are my options. I hang my head down and follow the men out. Before we leave, one of them fires a shot. Just one. I jolt my head back in horror to see the shot had been aimed at my mother's sitar. Music, according to them, is haram. My mother's screams and my sisters' wails fade in the backdrop as the door slams shut behind me.

I have grown to mistrust men in uniform.

05:05 PM: The line of riot police stands in our way, still as concrete, forming a barricade, like nothing could ever break them. Our people yell for them to let us through. They pay no heed.

People are beginning to stir.

"Get out of the goddamned way, you bastards!" Abe, who is in the lead, shouts over the crowd in his flawless English. "Let us go!"

Someone throws a rock. One of us. A small thing, no bigger than a child's hand. Certainly nothing that would do anyone any real harm. It ricochets off a police officer's helmet.

The crowd falls dead silent. The police officer glances down at the rock quietly. He shifts his gaze right, then left at his comrades, nodding curtly.

That's when it begins.

I am 14 when I finally see my chance to run away. I travel alone with nothing but a few basic provisions and some money my mother sent over with a relative. She wants me to go to Germany and seek refuge with some distant cousins there.

Somehow, I make it to Turkey. It is here that I submit completely to the possibility that I might die at any moment.

I ask around. I find a smuggler. He takes my money and tells me to wait for nightfall. For four months, I wait in the Jungle every night for my turn to cross the sea. One of the times we try to cross, the coast guards fire their guns into the air to scare us and chase after us.

Paddle harder!

What's the point? We don't stand a chance.

Stop screaming, I can't think!

The coast guards turn around and go back, leaving us in peace. I don't understand this. If they wanted to catch up with us, they could have. Easily.

05:17 PM: My throat is burning. The bastards set off their tear gas without a moment's hesitation. There is a clamour among the protesting families; faces squirming with anxiety as the squad drills straight into the panicking crowds.

I can barely make out the wailing children, waddling across the smoke into the arms of their mothers or fathers who are also screaming out in agony. I wish I could just run into my mother's embrace like that.

I don't see much after that. I don't see Abe anywhere. Or anyone else for that matter. What I do see is a blur of wavy motions and contours. My eyes feel like they have literally been set ablaze and my throat tightens as if a steel wrench is wringing out the oxygen from every cell in my body. The smoke threatens to suffocate me at any moment, but I stand my ground. The crowd has dispersed. Survival becomes key as my desire for freedom takes a back seat.

As the smoke begins to fade, I feel suddenly exposed, in full view to a few of the police squadrons who are standing still just opposite. They spot me.

One of the police officers approaches, his heavy boots resonating step by step on the concrete, his baton held casually in his hand. He looks me squarely in the eye, as if to say, *clear out boy*. But I don't. I'm tired of running.

He towers over me and stares me down through his helmet, gingerly caressing the baton with his fingers. He is giving me a chance to reconsider, a few seconds of stalling to prove I am the cowering refugee he wants me to be. Forever at his mercy.

Still, I stand my ground. I return his gaze: eyes fierce, shoulders contracted; feet rooted into the ground in a dogged stance. He flares up, raising an eyebrow, no longer simply bemused by my dissent.

Go ahead, I say without words. *Do your worst. I have seen it all.*

A sudden blow to the centre of my skull knocks me off my feet. There is a sensation of falling, and then I hit the floor with a jolt that numbs my entire left arm. The pain is instantaneous. The world around me is burning, but the scar on my temple pumps ice water. A gush of blood drips down my skull as my vision blurs. Moments later, everything goes black.

06:02 PM: I wake up on a stretcher in the nurse's ward in Section B. The section for unaccompanied minors. They must think I am exceptionally vulnerable to have finally decided to consider me underage.

My temple is throbbing. It feels as if my scar has been split wide open and is gushing out molten lava.

The nurse is dabbing at my forehead with a white compress. "*Makhdi, Makhdi.*"

The Greek nurse shakes her head, grinning as if she were a good-humoured principal who just caught a naughty pupil cutting class.

The cut must have been deeper than I thought, as I feel the burning of the sterilising liquid and the pull of renewed stitches deep in my sinews. I try to sit up using my elbows as levers, but my muscles tremble with exertion and I fall onto my back. I close my eyes and gnaw on my chapped lips, trying to consolidate the pain.

But I can't. My eyes pop open. My scar is smouldering. My entire being is smouldering.

I slap the nurse's hand away on instinct.

"My friend, no more!" I scream.

She is caught by surprise and considers for a moment whether to continue her wound care or let me be. In the end, she resigns and takes a few steps back.

I turn my head to face the wall and close my eyes, trying to relax. But then again, I always see more with my eyes closed.

Splatters of blood across paving stones; shrieks pleading for mercy; the cruel smirks of the men in uniform.

Death comes in so many shapes and colours, but the ones that really stick with me are the ones that I am responsible for. The men I pull the trigger on, the ones I maim, and, worse, the ones I am forced to kill, watching as the colour drains out of their faces one pant at a time.

Unlike the boy who killed my father, I never forget my victims' eyes. Their looks of horror, resentment, hatred even, are always there, waiting for me. Every time I close my eyes.

Take a life to stay alive. I wonder if it is worth it.

STAGE 3: GUILT

Usually, guilt comes as we look back over events surrounding the death of our loved one and we imagine how things might have unfolded differently. We sometimes come to the conclusion that maybe, just maybe, we could have done something that would have changed the outcome. We say, 'if only...' or 'what if...' and it gives us the feeling that the death was our fault because of something we did or didn't do. If we did take action, we may feel that events were therefore within our control, and we could have changed the outcome.[4]

careforthefamily.org.uk

---

4   https://Www.careforthefamily.org.uk/Family-Life/Bereavement-Support/Widowed-Young-Support/Wys-Articles/Wys-Newsletter-the-Role-of-Guilt.

3.1 Mahdi

Mahdi.

I hear a faint voice. Almost a whisper. Someone's calling me. Maybe. I don't know. I don't care anymore. I don't even turn my head. I'm falling again. Down a deep, dark ditch. But this time, I'm not asleep.

Mahdi.

It's everyday things, like not knowing what is going to happen. How long I'm going to be in this camp. Maybe it's forever. Maybe this is my life now. Waiting, just waiting, and not knowing. I feel like I might snap at any moment.

Mahdi.

It's my mother again. She won't leave me alone. It used to be only in dreams I'd see her face. Not exactly her face, just a shadow of her blank, featureless face with a disapproving aura. But now she is with me even when I am awake. I close my eyes, so hard it hurts, and try to remember what she felt like. What she smelled like. What she *looked* like. But there's nothing. It's as if those waves washed away all the memories I wanted to keep, and left those I wanted gone more than anything in a blaring spotlight.

Dark brown, almost black. I think that must be the colour of her eyes. My eyes are dark, so chances are hers would be as well. I am her son after all. Not to mention, when I was small, our neighbours in Dasht-e Archi did always compliment me on how much I looked like my mother, *mashAllah*.

I wonder if she would recognise me if she saw me now.

"Mahdi, *lala jan*. Get up," the kid on the bunk bed next to me says, nudging me with his elbow.

Section B comprises three rooms, each with 10–15 bunk beds where us minors shack up. Like those cheap hostels hip Europeans go to when backpacking across the world. My mattress squeaks with the slightest movement and pokes me in the ribs with its springs, but it's better than sleeping on that tattered blanket with the hundreds of people in Rubb Hall. And at least they are finally ready to admit I am a minor, like I'd told them all along.

"Mahdi!"

I wonder how he even knows my name. I never talk to any of them, let alone tell them *my name*.

"Get up, Mahdi! They're bringing in the new kid," another kid with a nasal voice says enthusiastically.

"Leave me alone." I groan and turn my back to him. I keep my head under the covers. I don't even care who is speaking to me these days, I just bury my head under the sheets most of the time.

Another voice.

"*Say kon!* Here he is."

I drape my pillow over my head and try to drown out the noise. Maybe I can get some sleep, even though it is the middle of the day. I seem to sleep better during the day. Somehow, daylight provides some kind of a shield against my nightmares. Somehow, during the day, the sound of the sea's waves drilling through my mind – splashing and clanking – is less deafening.

I let my eyes flutter shut. I let my body go numb, purging all tension from every muscle in my body. I let the dark circles behind my lids spiral and sway seductively, as they invite me to surrender into a long-anticipated sleep. Somewhere in the background, the kid with the nasal voice is speaking.

"*Say kon!* He thinks he is Dawood Sarkhosh!"

"Yeah, look at his backpack. Brand new. White check mark." The first kid whistles as if he has seen the Nike brand for the first time in his life. "He is one of the *lux* refugees. What's the matter, *o bacha*? Did your rich parents leave you behind to go on a cruise to America?"

I turn my head and see a group of three of them surrounding the new boy. Like vultures getting ready to pounce on a terrified gazelle. The new boy is quiet. He is young, must be no more than 13 or 14 years old. His body is hunched, with his backpack draped over one shoulder. His head is tilted down, gazing at his shoes. Also Nike. His huge, wireless headphones make him look like a scared little insect.

I turn back on my side and shut my eyes again. Though I feel for the kid, I've got enough problems of my own. I feel myself wasting away while waiting for something that may never come. The food here makes me feel sick. Bored of life. Tired of living.

More than anything, I need sleep. But there is so much noise, it is deafening.

"Does he know how to speak?" one of them jeers. "*Yallah*, say something,"

"What's your name, *o bacha?*"

I try to drown it out.

"Which *velayat* are you from?"

But they keep taunting.

"Hey, let me see that backpack."

And taunting.

"I said, give it to me!"

And taunting until something inside me breaks loose.

"Hey!" I jump off the bed. "Leave the kid alone!"

It's clear I catch the three boys off guard as their eyes widen in surprise and tilt their heads back to face me.

"Mahdi...we were just playing," says the first kid, his tone lowering from smug to innocent.

I have no idea what I have done to command such respect around here, but it seems to be working.

"Yeah, it was just a joke," says the one with the nasal voice. Then he turns to the new kid. "You're not mad, are you?"

The new kid continues to stare down at his shoes.

I stand my ground with my chest puffed up until the clan of vultures starts to disperse.

I figure the kid can take care of himself at this stage, so I make my way back up to my bunk bed and bury my head under the sheets again. Maybe I can finally get some sleep now.

Before long, I hear a shuffling noise around my bed. The kid must have taken the empty bed under mine. The movement stops and he plops onto his mattress finally.

"Mahdi?" calls a shy, trembling voice, slightly higher than pubertal vocal cords should be.

"*Che mekhai?* What do you want?" I respond, somewhat more unkindly than I intend to.

"*Tashakur kheli ziyad.* Thank you so much for what you did for me."

That makes me angry. If this kid thinks he's made a friend in me, he is delusional. I don't want any friends.

"I didn't do it for you. I just couldn't sleep, alright? Now leave me alone," I snap.

There is silence. I must have hurt his feelings. He seems the fragile type, so it is best he keeps his distance anyway. Someone like me and someone like him could never be close. I'd only end up hurting him, like I have everyone else in my life.

More silence. Good. Maybe I can sleep now.

"It's Jawed."

"What?"

"My name. It's Jawed," he says matter-of-factly, as if it were the question that has been burning in my mind all day.

"Nice name," I say sarcastically. "Can I sleep now?"

"Of course. *Shab khosh*. Good night."

Night? It's the middle of the day. Now he is teasing me.

Muffled music starts up from his oversized headphones. I know that song. *Sarzamine man*, by Dawood Sarkhosh. The song that speaks to the soul of every Afghan trying to remember what it was like to have a homeland. What it felt like to be someone, belong somewhere. *Sarzamine man*. My land.

If you are an Afghan, and I mean a *real* Afghan, that song always stirs something deep inside you. It shakes you awake from a long, dreamless sleep. A sensation long suppressed. A feeling long forgotten. As if we did belong somewhere once. We were something once. And who knows? We might be again someday, *inshAllah*, by the will of God.

My lips curl up into something like a smile before I let my eyes fall shut.

3.2 Zarifa

It's 9:30 PM and my son is not back yet. I don't know what has got into him lately. He never used to leave the tent at all, let alone stay out this late.

As far as I know, he doesn't even have any friends around here. I hope he hasn't gotten mixed up with those boys from the sections that are always stirring up trouble. I am calling him non-stop, but he is not answering his phone either.

Khodaya khodet komak kon. God, help us. Let him be okay.

I leave Yazna and Aylin with Massouma *khanoom* so I can go out and look for him. I pop my head round the neighbouring tents in the *Jungle* and ask Karima's sons on their way back from football practice. I even go around to the makeshift madrasas and mosques, where praying men are found prostrating at all hours, thinking constant *namaz* will rescue them from Moria . No one has seen him.

Resigned, I decide to head back, in case he comes home, finds it empty and gets worried. My heart is pumping so loud I think I might faint, so let myself tumble onto the blanket, trying to remember to keep breathing.

Hours or perhaps moments later, there is a shuffling sound outside the tent, making me jump back onto my feet on instinct.

"Milad, *pesaram*, is that you?"

He steps inside soundlessly, his red hood pulled tightly over his face.

"Where have you been?" I find myself screaming without intending to. "I've been worried out of my mind!"

He says nothing and simply retracts to his corner, burying his face into his phone as he always does. His indifferent attitude would outrage me, if it weren't for the fact that I get the feeling he is hiding something from me. His shoulders are more slouched, and his hood is more tightly wound around his face than ever before. His breath is shallow, making his chest heave up and down in an irregular motion.

I crouch down next to him and cup his chin with both of my hands. He is reluctant to lift his face up, but then, realising there is no point, he finally budges. And there it is. A bloody nose. Possibly fractured.

I try to keep my voice calm. "Milad *azizam*, what happened?"

He says nothing and draws his face back.

The pitch of my voice rises of its own accord. "Who did this?"

He keeps silent. Rage and despair seethe in me all at once. I don't know who or what I am angry at, but it is not him. It has never been him.

"You tell me right now who did this!"

"It doesn't matter," he mutters. "It won't happen again."

The tears that have been longing to break free come pouring out, like a dam that has just crumbled against the river's pressure. I cry myself dry and something in me relaxes.

"You're right, it doesn't matter," I sigh finally. "Because we're done with this hell. With the help of God Almighty." I point a finger up to the sky. "I am going to get you out of here, you'll see."

I pat his arm, unsure whether I am trying to reassure him, or myself.

"We will leave and never think of this God-forsaken place ever again. Soon, we will be able to look back and barely even remember it. It will be like a dream from a distant past that resurfaces from time to time and, even then, only in fragments. That is the only time we will think of Moria. The rest we will bury under heaps of sand, and we will just carry on and live decent lives. *Be omide khoda*, God willing."

I give him a side hug, bringing his head to rest on my shoulder.

Milad scoffs and pulls away. Confounded, I turn my head to gaze into his face, but he still averts his eyes. He must think I am naive to dare to dream such dreams. Perhaps he is right. But hope is all I have left to cling onto.

"Why didn't you tell me it was going to be so hard?" he suddenly groans.

I feel cornered. Ambushed, even. You try and you try and you try your very best as a mother, but it is not enough. It is never enough.

"How was I supposed to know it would be hard? I mean, sure, I believed there would be challenges along the way. Getting here would, of course, not be easy. But I thought that once we were here, once we confided in these people, told them the kind of life we left behind, and the kind of life we sought now instead; I thought if we'd let them see how we have nothing and no one else to trust, that we are forced to put our lives in the hands of foreigners, that everything would be fine. I wanted to believe that if we worked hard and led our own lives and didn't prove to be a burden for anybody, that we would be left alone. How was I supposed to know the *great Europa* was going to be like this?"

"Why didn't you tell me they hated us so much?" he snaps.

My voice catches in my throat. Tears are forming, even though I thought there was none left to cry.

"*Be khatera to.*" I stifle a sob. "Because of you. I wanted to protect you, that's why. All I have ever done is to try to protect you. I didn't want you to grow up thinking anyone could hate you because of your mocha-coloured skin or your slanted eyes, or the way you turn your *ahs* into *ohs* when you know damn well that has no place in this country. I wanted you to fit in. I wanted you to be a normal child and have a boring life; the kind of life I never had."

"Why didn't you tell me that boys, too, can be raped?"

He looks up for the first time, boring through my skin with his gaze. His eyes betray unspeakable grief. It is the same gaze that replaced the mischievous eyes of my playful little boy about the time his uncle diagnosed him as *irreparably damaged*.

Those eyes will never be the same again. He looks at me as if I am the one who wronged him. He looks at me as if I have been deceiving him from the day he was born, telling him white lies about a good life, a good future, a happy household. Making him believe in an ephemeral life that doesn't exist. Not for our kind, at least.

"Why didn't you tell me that boys, too, can be raped?"

The words lose meaning the instant they leave his mouth. I hear them in echoes, over and over and over and over.

They sound heavy and irate, and they groan and grind like metal on metal, like sandpaper on my nerves. But his face glimmers like innocence; his complexion shimmers like crystals, diamonds and precious stones. Those words don't belong to such a face; it's like a different species taking over an empty vessel, and such a beautiful one, depriving him of his sheen.

I was half-unconscious when his father hurled him across the room that night. All I remember are fragmented sounds that surface in nightmares from time to time. From that night onwards, his fear for his father melted away entirely and it was replaced with a sense of lethargy or apathy.

When yelled at, he heard nothing and showed no reaction.

When beaten, he just lay back and took it without a struggle. It was as if he no longer had anything to lose.

He comes to life for a second, just for one second, only to reprimand me.

"Why didn't you tell me that boys, too, can be raped?"

A mother's job is to protect her children, no matter how high the price. But I was weak, powerless. I was naive enough to think he would get tired of beating me. There were times he was sober, when he joked and laughed where I actually let myself believe he could even start to be a father one day. And when I realised that would never happen, when I finally realised I was entertaining childish fantasies about a family that would never be whole – a family I had already put at too much risk by staying and waiting for God to save us – my boy was already gone.

We tell our girls to stay girls forever; and in the same breath, we tell our boys to be men.

But my boy is neither. My boy is vacant. He is upright, feigning strength, but he is as brittle as a paper crane, shapely and sharp around the edges, and yet so lifeless. One touch would make him crumble like a sandcastle carried away by gusts of air; grain after grain after grain. Until there is nothing left. Just that vast expanse of the treacherous sea that made promises it couldn't deliver.

"*Khafeh sho*! Don't you dare ever say that again, you hear me? Not to anyone. Not to anyone."

3.3 Mahdi

My head is spinning. My stomach is churning. My heart is pumping so hard, it can barely keep up with my shallow breathing. Every beat sends pins and needles along the entire left side of my body.

They know it was me.

I think I might faint. No, I know I will. It's just a matter of time. Few more seconds, maybe, and I'll collapse. Maybe I should sit down.

Get a hold of yourself.

I don't even know what possessed me to do it. It was the guys. The ones from tent 747. Infamous addicts. Willing to do whatever it takes to get their grimy hands on more weed or alcohol or whatever else they think will make them forget about their miserable lives for a few short hours. They keep treating me like this dumb kid who can't stand up for myself. Like I could stand by, mute, and be told what to do with my head bowed low. Like I'd cave into their rules and regulations. Like I'd give a shit.

Footsteps echo in the distance.

It can' be. Not now. Not this soon.

I clutch at the door handle, but it slips right through my clammy hands. My head feels like it weighs more than my entire body. It's so hot, I can barely think.

Come on, Mahdi. To mitawani.

I wipe my hands on my frayed jeans, then grab for the door handle again. The door creaks open.

The bedroom is dark, aside from the dim lights flickering from a few smartphones here and there. It's past midnight, so all the other boys are either asleep or watching silly YouTube spoof videos on their phones.

I climb up to my bunk bed, knees trembling, and collapse onto the mattress. I lift the edge of the fitted sheet, empty my pockets and place the contents firmly underneath. I place the pillow over it to cover up the bulging parcel and then pull the covers so tightly over my head as if I want to cut off all access to air supply.

Maybe if I close my eyes hard enough, the whole thing will go away. Maybe I'll wake up with a start, realising it was all just a bad dream, because not even *I* could be stupid enough to actually go through with something like this. Maybe–

"ελάτε, everybody up!" A man yells, in a heavy smoker's voice as he steps into the room. The lights switch on without warning.

No one stirs at first. All the boys are either sleeping or so drawn by whatever they are watching online, it takes a while for the disruption to sink in.

It takes my eyes a few seconds to adjust to the blazing light and to the imposing figure in the room. It's him. That night-guard with the downward slanting eyes and the heavy mouth. The one who yells when he wants to speak, and roars when he wants to yell.

"I said UP!"

No. This can't be happening. How did he find out?

He bellows at the boys who are beginning to open their eyes and sit up on their beds. "Empty your bags. Your pockets. Everything"

I poke my head out of the blanket and rub my eyes, pretending to have just been awoken from a deep sleep. A few of the boys exchange blank looks. Some are so groggy they can't tell if any of this is really happening or whether they are having one of those weird dreams you have after living in Moria too long.

"Wha—.What for?" One of the boys says in a sleepy voice.
"EMPTY YOUR BAG."

That seems to jolt him awake. The terrified boy reaches underneath his bunk for his backpack and empties its contents on the floor. A few crumpled papers. Some coins. An empty juice box. And a half-eaten banana, going brown and mushy.

The guard grunts. He takes a few steps across the room, then turns to look in my direction. Something about his expression makes me nervous in a way I can't keep to myself. Something clicks. My vision is hazy; my heart is pumping ice water. He moves towards me, now determined. Could it be that he can hear my heartbeat all the way from over there?

"You!" he bellows, somewhat victoriously, as if he has just found the last missing piece of a puzzle.

"Empty your pockets."

I do as I am told and overturn my pockets. Empty. He grunts, disappointed. Maybe he'll leave me alone now. I mean, he only asked the other kid for his backpack, maybe he'll move onto someone else now and, not finding the culprit, he'll let us go. But no, he is not done with me yet. There is something in his beady eyes that won't rest until he has me in his grip.

"Get off the bed." he says, calmly.

I gulp. This is it. I am done for. I can't move.

"MOVE!" he roars.

I let myself slide close to the edge, one hand instinctively over the pillow, the other on my heart to keep it from breaking out of my chest.

"Turn it over."

I can't feel my heart anymore. My vision is failing. My entire body is numb. My hand places itself automatically on the pillow and begins to lift the corner, no longer taking commands from my brain.

This is it. This is the end. I wonder what they will do to me. But before my hand succeeds in flipping the pillow over, someone speaks.

"It was me."

All eyes turn towards the small, shaky voice. It's Jawed. I hadn't even noticed he was awake until just now. He is sitting with his shoulders hunched on the edge of his bed, his complexion pale and eyes heavy with interrupted sleep. There is muted silence as everyone waits for Jawed to explain why he would dare interrupt such an intense moment with his childish silliness.

"I did it," he says more confidently, this time. "I agreed to hold it."

That makes my hands curl into fists. What does he think he is doing? Who does this kid think he is? I never asked for his help. We're not friends, and never will be.

"YOU? But—How?"

The guard seems genuinely speechless. The shock is palpable in all of the boys' wide-eyed stares. Jawed is the last person anyone would have thought of as a suspect. And not without reason. The kid is harmless. Mostly keeps to himself. It is so easy to forget he even exists. The boy has a way of fading out of notice. I wish I had that superpower.

"How do you think?" Jawed says, almost smugly. "I was asked to hold it for some guys and I said yes."

His matter-of-fact voice rubs the guard the wrong way.

"Well, hand it over!" the guard yells out.

"I can't. It's gone."

"What do you mean *gone*?"

"Not in my possession. I gave it away."

The guard holds Jawed's gaze with his own aggressive countenance, but the boy doesn't flinch. The tension hangs thick and heavy in the air. The two stare into each other's eyes so long, it seems they have stopped time altogether.

"Alright, kid." the guard says, finally. "Let's go."

He grabs Jawed by the arm and pulls him up to his feet, then shoves him towards the door. Jawed goes compliantly and wordlessly, head hung low.

I heave a deep sigh of relief. *That was close.* I was sure they had me. Never in a thousand years could I have predicted things to unfold the way they did. And Jawed, of all people, to get blamed for my stupid actions. But no. This is wrong! Dumb as the kid is, I can't let him take the fall for me. Before I can stop myself, I jump off the bed.

"No, wait—"

Jawed tilts his head back and interrupts me mid-speech.

"It's okay, Mahdi. I'll be okay." He throws me a meaningful look before the guards thrusts him out of the door, mumbling.

"Don't count on it."

I toss and turn the rest of the night, hand firmly holding down that corner of my pillow. I fall asleep at one point, and dream of dark waves breaking aggressively on the edge of the shore. Splashing. Clanking. And splashing. But among the waves, I hear something else. Something like music. Some verses of a song, muted by the imposing sound of the sea.

I blink awake to the early morning light burning through my sheets. I feel like I haven't slept for hours. No waves. It was just another dream. But the music, I can still hear. It's warped, muffled even, as if coming through headphones. But I can still hear it. Somehow it soothes me, knowing I am not the only one awake at this hour. When I listen closely, I hear the words.

Sarzamine man, khasta khasta az jafayet. Dawod Sarkhosh.

That can only mean *he* is back.

I want to know what they did to him. Why he did what he did for me. I am touched and furious at the same time, and I have no idea where to even start with all the questions I have and all the answers I need.

I tilt my head down over the side of my bed to face him.

"Hey!"

He pauses his music and lifts his head up innocently. Something about his ghost-white face and bloodshot eyes makes me soften my tone.

"I didn't ask you to do that."

"I didn't do it for you," he says simply.

I raise an eyebrow, blank-faced.

"Oh?"

"Do you know the amount of respect I am going to get now that I am such a law breaker?" A hint of a smile appears through his cracked lips. "No one would dare grab my backpack again."

I let my head dangle there, not sure whether to take what he said as a joke or at face value.

Jawed plays his music again, unperturbed by my continued presence or the puzzled look on my face. I notice, for the first time, how when he plays that music, it seems to remove any trace of worry or fear from his face altogether. Eyes closed, face calm, really relishing the beats and verses of the melancholic song.

"Aren't you a little too young to be a patriot?" I say, nodding towards his persistent choice of music.

"Never too young to love your country." The edges of his mouth curve up, this time into a proper smile, bringing some much needed colour back into his face.

"Smoke?" I hold out my pack as a sign of brotherhood.

"Is that allowed in here?"

I wink and grin.

"Only if you don't get caught,"He half-chuckles and reaches up to take the cigarette out of my hand.

3.4 Frishta

It's morning. Mummy and Mohsen are still asleep, but I am awake. Lately, I wake up before them. Before any of our neighbours too. I wake up when the sky is still dark, and the air is quiet, and nothing can be heard except for the chirping of birds and rustling of leaves on trees.

Sounds nice, except that I wake up with a bad feeling, like I've forgotten something important, or like something bad is about to happen. I lie awake for hours, waiting for whatever it is to finally come and show itself. When, all of a sudden, it does. Mummy's phone rings. It's okay, I can take it. Whatever it is, it can't be worse than worrying. Or can it?

It rings again. Then twice. Then three times.

Mohsen doesn't stir. It takes a lot more than ringing a phone to wake Mohsen up, sometimes shouting over his head *MOHSEN! GET UP!* doesn't even do the trick. But Mummy begins to shuffle under her blankets, then, registering what the noise is, she sits up and reaches for her phone.

"Don't answer it!" I blurt out.

She shushes me and picks up the phone.

"Allo?" she says in her sleepy voice.

My heart races. I hear a man's voice over the receiver. He has an Iranian accent.

"*Khanoome* Ghafori?"

"Yes, who is this?" Mummy replies hesitantly.

"I am calling from the asylum services office. It is about your interview."

Mummy's eyes widen as she turns to look in my direction. My heart is doing somersaults and my face, I am sure, is pale white. Even more so than Mummy's right now.

"Yes, what about it?"

"I am calling to tell you, you have received a positive decision. You and your children are now recognised refugees in Greece."

Her face breaks into a grin.

"Oh *Shukr-e Khuda*, thank God!"

"My pleasure. You will receive your papers shortly. *Mobarak bashe*, Mrs Ghafori."

"*Tashakur!*"

When she hangs up the phone, she just sits there, not blinking, her face brighter than ever.

Mohsen is now up, rubbing his eyes, not sure what is happening. I just stare at Mummy, wide-eyed, still unsure whether to tell my heart to stop doing gymnastics inside my chest.

"Mummy, what—" Mohsen begins. Before he can finish, Mummy jumps to her feet.

"We did it! We did it!" she squeals, happier than I have seen her, maybe ever. "Do you know what this means, *bachem*? Today is the first day of the rest of our lives!"

She gestures for me and Mohsen to come close and draws us both in for the tightest hug ever. I hear her crying and laughing at the same time. Her laughter makes me smile; her tears make me pout.

"Why are you crying, Mummy?" I ask.

"Because I am happy. And so lucky to have the two of you!"

Now that the sun is finally up, Mummy and Mohsen are out trying to find *kaka* Abolfazl to tell him the news. I asked for permission to go out for a walk around the *Jungle*. For once, everything I see is beautiful.

Dads are up early making fires. Mums are rolling flour into dough. And children are out jumping in the puddles left over from the night's rain, making their clothes muddy and laughing to themselves.

Something about this morning feels so much more welcoming than any other day I have been in this camp!

As I come near the fence between the *Jungle* and the inside of the camp, I notice a group of children sitting on the floor at a distance, muttering in hushed voices. I squint against the sun. The fatter boy with shaggy black hair and Bermuda shorts has to be Ghassem. Though his head is bowed and I cannot make out his face from over here. The way he is talking over everyone, as he usually does, gives him away.

My two best friends, Arezoo and Elaha are sitting side by side, listening carefully to whatever he is saying. And then there is Abbas. The sun is in his face, making his big hazel eyes shine like gold.

Abbas' family lives just a few tents away from us. I remember the day our caravan burned down in the fire, and we were forced to move to one of the tents in the *Jungle* instead. It was mouldy and cold and I didn't like it one bit. Abbas saw me that same night sitting outside, crying quietly to myself so Mummy wouldn't hear me. He came and sat next to me.

"I know it doesn't look too good right now, but you'll get used to it," he'd said comfortingly. "And hey, there's a bright side to it."

"What's that?" I'd asked, wiping away my tears with my sleeves.

He winked and nudged me.

"You get to have the most handsome boy in the *Jungle* as your neighbour,".

We both laughed, and that's how we became friends.

The four of them are huddled together in a circle, probably playing that silly war game again. Some of them pretend to be the Afghans, others the Arabs. And then they battle. But it is not as simple as it sounds. There is a whole strategy to the game. They come up with war tactics. They set up patrol groups and command posts. They come up with code words for their teams, tactics for strikes and counter-strikes, attacks and counter-attacks. The catch is that someone always ends up getting hurt, either by falling or taking their roles too seriously. Just like in the real Moria wars.

It is a silly, dangerous game that I stopped playing long ago. Mummy has never liked it either. She says it might bring bad omens.

Drawing a few steps closer, I come to a halt and watch over them. Ghassem is using a dead branch to sketch out a map with stick figures on the dirt.

"*Bacheha*, guys," he says, putting on a fake army man voice and raising his eyebrows. "Word has it, a war has broken out. A *real battle*." He pauses dramatically, waiting for *ohs* and *ahs* from the audience. The other kids stare at him blankly.

He clears his throat and continues.

"The Arabs have attacked. Stolen our girls. They are being held prisoners, right over *here*," he scratches an X into the ground with the tip of the branch. "It's up to the boys to get them back. Abbas and I will come around the fence *here* from the *Jungle*, and we'll meet up with Nisar, Arshiya and Asif, just behind *Level 4*. We will bide our time there to catch the Arabs off guard, and when they least expect it – *BAM*. We'll raid their outposts. Ready, *men*?"

On the last word, his voice cracks.

"Hold up," Arezoo cuts in, frustrated. "You want the girls to pretend to be prisoners?" She twirls a strand of her black hair around her finger, as she always does when she is annoyed. "No way."

"I'm with Arezoo," Elaha adds, pressing her pink-framed glasses back on her nose with one finger. "That's hardly fair."

"Come on, girls," Ghassem begins, puffing out his chest. "Men fight. Women get rescued. It's not my fault, it's how God intends it."

I roll my eyes. Ghassem is only ten, but he keeps calling himself a man.

"Oh please," Arezoo harrumphs, unimpressed. "Women can fight just as well as men. And by the way, you don't get to call yourself a man when your voice is higher pitched than mine."

Ghassem's cheeks burn red, and he frowns at the ground. I cannot help but let out a snigger, giving my position away. Arezoo really cracks me up. All faces turn towards me now.

"Hey, it's Frishta!" Arezoo grins.

"Hey, princess," Abbas winks at me, making my cheeks burn. I turn my head away quickly before he notices. "We heard you received a positive decision. *Mobarak!*" He grins with those dimples that make my heart jump suddenly.

News travels faster than anything in this camp, especially when it comes to asylum decisions.

"Is it true? Are you leaving?" Arezoo cuts in, looking suddenly disappointed.

"Well, yes," I say hesitantly. "But we don't know when. We haven't received our tickets yet."

"So unfair. My family got here long before yours. And we're probably going to die and be buried here," Ghassem huffs.

"So, this may be your last game with us," Elaha pouts at me, ignoring Ghassem.

Suddenly, I realise that she is right, and all the excitement

I felt in the morning begins to disappear. I hadn't really thought of it that way. Sure, we all need to move on, but what about my friends? What about *kaka* Abolfazl? What about *Abbas*? It is true they had all arrived before us, and it is true single mothers were usually considered special cases so that is probably why Mummy's decision came faster than everyone else's. But was that really fair on them? They have been living in the same tents, under the same rain, suffering through the same cold nights. It doesn't really feel right that I should move on before them just because my *baba* decided to walk out on us one day. It dawns on me then, that the thing about receiving happy news is that there is always a catch. The happiness is momentary.

"I'm not playing," I say, trying to shake off their questions and comments.

"Obviously not if the girls are supposed to be *rescued*," Arezoo says sarcastically, shooting Ghassem a loaded look.

Ghassem clicks his tongue exasperatedly.

"*La illah ila Allah*," he says, reciting a Quranic phrase he has learned recently from Friday prayers and has been overusing ever since. "Fine, you can fight too. Happy?"

"I'm not playing either way. This game is stupid." I fold my arms a little more childishly than intended and look away.

"Oh, come on," Abbas begins with his sweet voice. "Frishta *jan*, Frishta-*ye man*, my angel. You can play one more time, can't you? For old time's sake?"

My heart always flutters when he calls me his angel.

"Um yeah, I guess. Alright."

"See, I knew Abbas would convince her," Ghassem nudges Elaha, a stupid grin spreading on his round face.

I clear my throat suddenly and narrow my eyes at Ghassem.

"Let's just play."

We rise to our feet, ready to begin the game. Before we have a chance to start, another boy, around Ghassem's age, comes running towards us. This one, I have not met before.

"I just spoke to Arshiya. They are down one combatant. Someone has to join the Arab team."

"Right. So, who's going to play on the Arabs' side?"

Ghassem looks around for volunteers. His gaze lands on Abbas and raises his eyebrows.

"Don't even think about it," Abbas says, sticking his tongue out. "Born an Afghan and will die an Afghan." He smacks his lips together as his eyes shine with pride.

A sneering voice comes from behind him.

"Mr Big Shot in front of your little friends, aren't ya?"

Abbas' big brother, Mirfaiz, suddenly appears round the corner.

Mirfaiz is lean, mean and usually unforgiving, even with his own flesh and blood. He is what we children liked to call a *professional* bully. He pokes fun at younger kids in public. He gives his brother black eyes in private, then makes him lie and tell his mum it was a football accident. And when he isn't terrorising children, he is out picking fights with boys twice his size. Just to feel like a real man.

None of us like Mirfaiz, and most of us are too scared to be near him. We just stare at our feet whenever he shows up and count the minutes until he leaves. Abbas can't walk away though since they share a tent and a family. Having a brother like Mirfaiz must be even worse than having to eat Moria's dinners every night of your life.

Abbas turns around to face Mirfaiz.

"*Dadash*? I didn't—"

Poor Abbas always stammers when talking to his brother.

"When you're playing your dumb games, you like being the hero," Mirfaiz scoffs at his little brother. "But where were you when *baba* was getting beaten to a pulp next to the food line last month?"

"*Baba* told me to stay with *madar jan*," Abbas insists "He told me not to leave the house, otherwise—"

"Yeah, he told me not to leave either, but I didn't listen. I listened to my gut and went out there to fight beside him," Mirfaiz says scornfully. "Boys were made to fight. Not to hide and cower in the tent with the women. But you wouldn't know much about that. So go back to playing a hero. *Wallah*, you can't be one in real life."

Mirfaiz stomps off, leaving Abbas with downcast eyes.

Abbas's body slumps to the ground. It hurts to see him like this. I kneel beside him and lay one arm over his shoulder.

"Are you okay?"

Abbas shrugs.

"Hey, don't listen to him," Ghassem begins, nudging him. "You're a warrior, and nothing defeats a warrior, remember?"

"Yeah, and besides, you don't want to be like him. He's a bully," Arezoo offers.

"Let's just play," Abbas says with a weak smile, rising to his feet.

"Right." Ghassem is back in the lead. "Girls, you hide out behind the shower containers over there. Asif, you join the Arab team. Abbas and I will go down to *Level 4*. Everyone ready?"

We all nod our heads yes.

"Positions everyone!"

Arezoo, Elaha and I take our hiding spot behind the shower containers, giggling. It is a silly game, but it is a lot of fun to play, I have to admit.

"Hey," Elaha whispers shyly. "What do you girls think of Ghassem?"

"Silly, annoying, oh and so full of himself," Arezoo says simply.

"Yeah," I second. "But to his credit, he is a good leader."

"Right?" Elaha's eyes brighten.

Arezoo's eyebrow shoots up at Elaha.

"Well, look who has a crush on snotty-faced Ghassem," she teases.

I laugh so hard my tummy hurts.

"Do not. And don't call him that!" Elaha pouts, but then she starts to laugh too.

"What is taking so long?" Arezoo says impatiently. We poke our heads out from behind the caravan but see nothing. "The boys should have given us the signal by now."

She is right, they should have. It is odd that we have not heard from them yet. I look around and suddenly feel a knot in my tummy.

Something is wrong. Before, families were out and about, but now there is no one in sight. There is a strange quietness around the *Jungle,* and the air feels heavy. I have seen this before. *Kaka* Abolfazl calls it the silence before the storm.

Just then, there is pattering against the front of the caravan we are hiding behind, like heavy rain or ice beating against the metal. Except it is not rain or ice, but pebbles and stones being thrown from every direction. A war has broken out; this time for real.

"We have to leave, now!" I shout to the others, and they nod, pale-faced.

We hold hands and start running down the slope. From a distance, we can make out crowds of men gathering. Mobs of angry men arm themselves with sticks and stones. They seem to be moving towards the hole in the fence that leads to *Level 4*.

My heart sinks. The boys! We run to the fence and squint through the chain-link, not daring to breathe.

"I see them! They're fine!" Elaha cries.

Ghassem and Abbas are hiding behind one of the fruit stalls, waiting for the mob to move away. They look in our direction and spot us. I wave them over as the mob on our side is slowly thinning.

When Ghassem sees his chance, he takes Abbas by the hand and drags him towards the opening in the fence. Just as they are about to reach us, something brings them to a sudden halt.

It's Abbas. He is frozen still, unable to move.

"*Yallah* Abbas, this is no time for games!" Ghassem yells over the clamour. Abbas doesn't budge.

"What's going on? Why has he stopped?" Arezoo shrieks.

They are bickering now. I can't make out what they are saying, but Ghassem seems to be pleading and pulling on Abbas' sleeve, and Abbas keeps pulling back. He shifts his big, golden eyes towards me. His expression changes from anxious and unsure, to calm and determined.

Come on, Abbas, what are you doing?

And that's when it happens, in less than a second. Before Ghassem can stop him, before I can hear my heart snapping, Abbas turns on his toes and sprints towards the angry mobs. Ghassem's eyes open wide, his mouth making the shape of an O.

All four of us scream for Abbas to come back. But it is too late, the warring men take him in as one of their own. In the time it takes for the next stone to whizz just past my head, barely missing me, he is gone.

3.5 Maryam

I arrived in Lesbos on 30 May 2018, exactly five days after one of the bloodiest incidents Moria camp has ever seen. It became known as the Kurdish-Arab fight. Though, admittedly, the name was misleading – it was more of an attack than an actual fight.

A group of about 30 Arab men allegedly launched an ethnic cleansing ritual hurling stones, rocks and anything else they could find at Kurdish minorities, whose way of life they found unholy. Then, when they finally ran out of long ranged weapons, they broke into their tents, beat the men with batons and left them to bleed out.

Word had it, one of the assailants' consciences caught up with him when launching an offensive on an elderly Kurdish man, Abu Muhammad, and told his ring leader to leave him alone. To which the ring leader responded:

"He doesn't pray or fast – it is *halal* to kill him."

In the clinic, we talked about it for months after that. Dozens – both Kurd and Arab – were injured and rushed to emergency services. Despite all the threats, however, none were fatally wounded or killed. *Thank God.*

The incident led about a hundred Kurds to flee the camp and, with the support of aid workers, set up shelter in another camp on the other side of town.

Many feared the incident could only mean the conflict in Syria had found its way into Europe. There were concerns that this group of assailants had once belonged to ISIS, and that they were slowly planting the seeds of extremist Islamism to flourish on this side of the world as well. But humanitarian workers knew better than to give in to such scaremongering.

Fights in the camp are reported on a weekly basis, even now. Throw thousands of people into a simmering pot of water, wrought with daily stressors, triggers and tensions, and tell me if it doesn't overflow. It is not even a matter of *if,* but rather *when.*

It is precisely this familiarity with the simmering pot of Moria, knowing that tensions could erupt at any moment, that means the mass casualty training sessions have to be repeated at regular intervals for medical organisations like ours; just to make sure all staff members – old and new – are ready to spring into action any time the scalding water pours out over the edges.

"But how many casualties does it take for it to be considered a mass casualty," Yusifinsisted.

Our trainer, a meek, Belgian man, was not too keen on being flown back in for the second time in three months.

"You want a specific number?" he asked impatiently.

Yusif nodded.

"Yes, a number."

"Alright, let's say four or five," he relented.

Yusif and I exchanged sceptical looks. The stakes were lower than we thought.

When it comes to halting all operations and preparing the clinic for casualties only, five is a decent enough number. Four, I'm not too sure qualifies as a mass casualty. Surely, *I mused,* we have enough capacity to rush the four to the emergency rooms and still carry on seeing our regular patients.

The problem is, the clinic is very selective about what they define as an *emergency*.

The night of the first fire, I remembered how, at the start, I'd felt proud to be a humanitarian worker. The fact that we had all mobilised so quickly to help potential burn victims in Moria so late at night was exemplary. The way in which we got ourselves organised so effectively, and how we each found a way to be useful, even at the most quiet times, was laudable. But later, in the early hours of the morning, everything changed.

It was announced that the clinic was closed to everyone and everything aside from extreme emergencies: cases that will not survive the night unless they receive medical assistance.

A single mother came in with her two children. Her daughter, Frishta, a sweet girl aged eight or nine, was covering her eye with one hand. She said a tiny piece of glass had got wedged in it.

On that night, their caravan had caught fire and the girl had pulled her little brother out just in time. But the window had exploded and shattered, and that's how the glass flew in her direction. The family, alongside tens of others, had been rendered homeless that night and were taking shelter in abandoned tents in the *Olive Grove* – or, what the camp's residents like to call, *The Jungle*.

Then, they had come to our clinic asking for medical support. We had a total of four doctors and two nurses on site, preparing for another potential mass casualty. And yet, despite our overcapacity, we still refused to help the family on account of the case not fitting within our definition of the word *emergency* in that particular moment.

I exhausted all means before facing the mother and telling them, with a more than heavy heart, that the answer was no. No, we could not tend to her little girl, even though the clinic was visibly empty at that time. No, we would not give Frishta a safe haven in our clinic, not even after the terrifying night they'd had. No, we would not give her the hero's welcome she deserved, because we simply had other priorities.

When I related the bad news, the mother had cried, and I actually felt my heart break.

Today, a day like any other, we receive word from the camp's authorities that the pot is overflowing – again.

Static noise is followed by a call on clinic staff's walkie-talkies.

"All staff please report to the back office. Over," announces the dainty voice of our clinic manager.

Tens of staff members abandon their posts and report to the back of the clinic, an open area with wooden benches and chairs. Some let their weary bodies flop down on the benches, while others remain standing, on high alert. This can't be good.

The clinic manager is a mild-mannered man who had just flown in from headquarters two weeks before for his first, if not second, assignment *ever*. Under normal circumstances, he might be more than pleasant, perhaps someone I could have a beer and banter with. One week into Moria and he is, more often than not, nervous, jittery and second guessing his strategy in case he should do something wrong and bring the clinic into disrepute.

"We have received a security alert from the camp," he says, barely audible and to no one in particular, as if he is reading something off a script. "A fight. No details are known. No staff to enter the camp. Please clear out the clinic for potential casualties."

The way he shifts his weight from one foot to the other, and the way he keeps running his fingers through the loose strands of his gold-tinted hair, gives away his uncertainty.

And who can blame him? Two security alerts in two weeks. This is not what you usually expect when you accept a summer assignment to a Greek island on the coast of the Aegean Sea.

My hand shoots up before I can contain it.

"What do you mean *clear out the clinic*? Where are we supposed to send the patients?"

"They could exit through the back door."

Yusif is the next to speak.

"Exit and go where? Surely not back into the camp?"

The manager hesitates. And that is the exact pause we, the staff, need to strike. Like a wounded lion surrounded by antelopes, waiting to take their revenge.

"We have patients who are pregnant, mothers with newborn babies, families with toddlers," shouts the midwife, her head poking out from the back.

The triage nurse agrees. "We can't just send them into the middle of the fight. It's not safe!"

"The clinic is the safest place for them right now!"

Everyone nods except two or three staff members, who are staring blankly at the manager, waiting for his cue.

The manager shuffles, torn between giving in to popular demand or standing his ground to establish some much needed authority.

"Alright," he relents finally. "Yes, escort the patients into the side tent. Keep the waiting areas, pharmacy and consultation rooms clear for casualties – please."

That's our cue. Yusif and I rush to the main waiting area to be the bearers of bad news.

"*Khanoomha wa aghayoon – Mesdames et messieurs –* سيدات و سادتي – Ladies and gentlemen. We have received word that there is a fight in the camp. We need to therefore clear out this area to make space for potential casualties. Please follow me into the side tent, where you can wait until things have calmed down."

A flustered woman grapples with a toddler fidgeting in her arms. "Will the doctor still see my baby?"

"I am afraid he can't. Not today. He is preparing to receive wounded," I say, apologetic but firm –if I hesitate, I won't hear the end of it.

"But what about my son's cough?" says the woman, struggling to keep her boy from slipping away.

Another chimes in.

"And my daughter's skin rash?"

"We've been waiting since seven in the morning!"

A woman, in the late stages of pregnancy, is red and puffy from the day's heat. "I live at the very top of the slope, I can't trek here every day in these conditions," she exclaims.

The patients squabble among themselves, and then with me. I side-glance at Yusif with pleading eyes, hoping he has a way out of this.

He takes the hint and holds his hand up quietly, waiting for the room to fall silent. Something about his towering presence demands more respect than the rest of us.

"I understand this is difficult, and that you have all been waiting a very long time to see the doctor. *Wallah* I do," he says, in his calming but firm tone – much firmer than myself. "I know what it is like to be ignored, I once slept up on top of that slope too."

He throws the pregnant lady a meaningful glance, which seems to soothe her on the spot.

There it is. The *I once was a refugee just like you* card. The card I, as an immigrant, can never play. Every time I try to get through to them, all I get is back talk. And when I try to appeal to reason, all I get in return is *how would you know? You never lived in a tent.* Which sets on mute me instantly.

It is clear that speaking the language does not guarantee the other side will listen. There is something about the lived experience of being a refugee that I very much lack. A hole that the experience of immigration alone is not likely to fill. To command respect, you need to have suffered in the same way. You need to have spent nights trembling in fear, spent the days waiting in endless queues in futility. You need to have risked your life more than once to save that of your children's. Otherwise, you don't know what you are talking about."For your own safety, we need you to cooperate," Yusif continues, like a supreme leader beginning to rally the crowd. "We might start receiving injured patients very soon. *La samh Allah,* God forbid, they could be your neighbours, friends, even your husbands." He pauses to allow for sudden gasps and murmurs to take their course. "So please. Follow Maryam into the side tent now and wait there until further notice."

I start leading ten – maybe 20 – disgruntled patients and their squirming children into the tent, and sit them out on the benches lining the floor.

During mass casualty incidents, this tent is the one that metamorphosises into the green tent for less severe patients. For now, due to lack of a better option, we will have to use it as a refuge for patients until it is deemed safe enough for them to return to their own, much smaller, and much less secure, tents.

A mother chastises her wriggling toddler, who keeps climbing up and down the bench. "Sit still." She turns to me. . "What are they fighting about this time, *khanoom* Maryam?"

"We don't have any information at this stage," I say, loud enough for everyone to hear.

"I know what it's about," says an Afghan lady, with bright orange lipstick and matching headscarf.

I sit next to one of the women and listen intently. In moments like this, I opt to become a fly on the wall and gather any information I think might be useful for the clinic to know, in case it helps us plan ahead.

"Of course you do, Kareema *jan*," winks the pregnant lady, who is now fanning herself with some clinic flyers she must have picked up from the waiting area. "If you don't, then who would?"

"Hey, shut up, this is no joke," chastises Ms Orange jestingly. She drops her voice down to a whisper, but still talks loud enough for the whole room to hear. "Apparently one of *our* boys, a young thing, no more than 18 or 19 years old, filmed one of *their* women in the toilet." She nudges her head towards an Arabic-speaking lady sitting on the corner bench.

The Afghan women gasp. Some clutch their hearts, others cover their children's ears.

"Shhh! There are children here, Kareema!"

"Sorry, sorry." Kareema drops her head. "But can you imagine?" She smacks her orange lips together, almost as if she is enjoying being in the spotlight.

"Afghan men," sighs the pregnant woman, clicking her tongue. "Always bringing shame to our community."

"Easy, *abji*, sister," says the one with the toddler. "So a young boy got carried away. No need for the Arabs to wage a war."

"You know what they're like about their women. I wish my husband was like that about me," sighs Kareema. "I could be filmed while taking a shower from start to finish and the film could even win an Oscar and he still wouldn't care. He wouldn't even turn up for the awards ceremony!"

"Shut up!" teases the pregnant woman. The two women chuckle and the rest join in with giggles and smiles.

"*Tuba astaghfirullah*, how can you laugh at a time like this?"

says the toddler's mother, not unsmiling herself.

We stay and joke for a while, until time seems to slow down and the fight seems to transform into static noise – still dangling over our heads, but in a harmless, unimposing way.

That is until one of our Dari interpreters, a young Afghan girl named *Shukufa*, rushes into the tent, trembling and pale-faced. The entire room falls silent."What's wrong *Shukufa jan?*" I ask, suddenly concerned. *Shukufa* is known for her contagious smiles, so with her current state, I fear something terrible must have happened.

"You look like you've seen a ghost, girl!" says the pregnant woman, echoing my concern.

"*Yak bacha ra zadan.* A boy has been stabbed," she stammers, tears rolling down her terrified face. "One of our own."

3.6 Mahdi

"*Dard dara?* Does it hurt?"

I keep asking that, knowing Jawed cannot utter a word in response; knowing that even if he could, it is probably the worst thing to ask him right now. This is, by no means, what he would choose to talk about if he could talk at all. Instead, he stares at me blankly, his eyes bulging and his muscles strained, trying hard to fight back, even when it is obvious that he has no fight left in him at all.

It's a day like any other when the fight between the Arabs and Afghans breaks out. Afghans are gathering just outside of the sections, arming themselves with anything they can find – rods, bats, even kitchen knives – to start the moving procession up the slope. Word has it, the Arabs are waiting out by Levels, preparing some kind of an ambush.

Jawed tries to drag me back into our room, saying boys have no business in men's fights. I laugh bitterly and shove him aside.

"Maybe you don't, bacha," I say smugly, blowing my cigarette smoke straight into his eyes. I throw the stub on the floor and wave him away. But he stays by my side. Trembling and loyal. Until the very end.

Our eyes lock. His eyes shifting nervously, mine creased in anticipation. It must be my determination that finally makes him heave a deep sigh and tell me that if I insist on joining the ranks, that he'll come and fight with me.

"Maybe you're not such a bacha after all," I smirk.

We flank the mob as the men start to move towards the Levels, the last known hideout of the enemy. But before we even get halfway there, an avalanche of pebbles flies into the air and takes out several of our men.

The foes come out of nowhere, like spirits conjured up out of the thin air. They must have known they were outnumbered, so they used strategy to their advantage.

It all happens so fast. Action shots of frozen scenes; standing still and whirring in a time lapse all at once. Cries of war. Gapes of shock. Looks of determination.

We are caught off guard, but we try to fight back. A rainstorm of rocks are hurled from both sides. On our side, men armed with baseball bats holler and run out in all directions.

A strike. A counterstrike. Squirming bodies sprawling on the concrete. Theirs and ours. And then – watch out, that boy has a knife! *Steel on flesh. A blade to the chest. Whose chest? Men suddenly losing their manhood, screeching, calling for help.*

A cry of pain.

I know that voice.

My lungs are airless. My head is spinning. My heart is screaming. My voice is drowned out by shrieks of horror and rage.

Kumak kunid! Somebody, help him!

Jawed has that same terrified look in his eyes as the first time we'd met. When the other boys teased him and he'd pulled his hoodie down to cover half of his face. But even then, I could still see his eyes shifting nervously underneath the fabric.

He seems lost and not of this world. With his head bowed low, he was never the type to stir up trouble. I remember the day he'd stumbled over to the bunk bed just below mine, after just taking a fall for me, and lay down without saying a word. I remember seeing all hints of dread and tiredness melt away from his face whenever he listened to the melancholic notes of Dawood Sarkhosh's Sarzamine man gushing through his oversized headphones as he sang of the sorrows of a nation without a home.

I have become homeless
I have gone from home to home
Without you always with grief
I have gone from shoulder to shoulder
My one and only love
From you my sign
Without you there is no salt
In my poetry and song
My Land

Jawed became the embodiment of the family I had abandoned. The family I had not spoken to for more than a year. The family who I had not cared to even reach out to, to tell them whether I was dead or alive after I'd run away from the Taliban. But in the end, I had abandoned him too, like everything and everyone else in my life.

Jawed's features are still youthful, but his eyes have aged so much since that first day, three months ago.

"Does it—. Does it hurt to die?"

I'm not sure if I want to know the answer.

He hears me. Does he hear me? Does he choose not to hear me? His mouth is a gaping hole, gasping desperately for air. The colour is draining from his face; his complexion is turning grey. His whole body is sprawled into a heap on the floor.

He is shaking all over now, writhing weakly from side to side, pulsating with the chattering of his teeth. He is so cold. Even though I am with him. His body temperature has dropped so dramatically, there is no way to restore it.

His body begins to convulse, so I move him away from the mob and cover him up in whatever rags I can find, praying that it helps somehow.

If only I had not dragged him into this fight; if I had just made him go back, maybe he wouldn't have followed me and got stabbed for nothing. Maybe I would not have to endure watching him struggling to stay alive, even if only for a few more breaths.

Where the hell are the paramedics?

Seconds feel like hours. We are huddled in the corner of the road now – waiting. His head is scooped onto my lap, and his torso is nestled in my arms like an infant, swaddled tightly in towels and rags. I cradle him and sway my body from side to side, trying to distract him from the pain. If there is any. *Is there any?*

Despite all my efforts to shield him from the cold, he trembles. I cup his face with my hands, trying to share my skin's heat; his eyes dart back and forth, trying to register something familiar in my face – still, he trembles. I grab one of his icy hands and begin to rub it between my palms – still, he trembles. The harder I rub, the more his frozen fingers stiffen; and the more his pulse slows down, like a faltering pendulum coming to a gentle halt. My scar is burning; my stitches are pulling my temple apart. Now, we both tremble.

As a kid trying to make it on your own in the world, you need to get used to the trembling. It becomes your only salvation, the only way your body has to remind you that it is not immune to sensations; that it still functions as per basic instinct. Trembling is what reminds you that, despite all efforts to hurry up and grow up, that you're still just a kid, that you don't have to put up a fight all the time. That it is okay to just give into your childish instinct and be afraid sometimes.

Jawed's lips move unexpectedly, as he sucks in a rush of air and tries to formulate words for the first time in hours. I lean in closer.

"Sing to me."

His voice is so ragged and hoarse, like he hasn't spoken for weeks. Sing? Sing what?

He gawks at me with his liquid eyes, almost expectantly, just like my father's eyes before he drew his last breath. I suddenly know what he wants.

Sarzamine man,
Who composed your grief?
Sarzamine man,
Who opened the door to your heart?
Sarzamine man,
Who has been faithful to you?
Sarzamine man.

I part my reluctant lips and try, but nothing comes out, not even a gasp. I hear the tune in my head, but I cannot bring myself to formulate the words into sounds.

"Sorry, *lala jan*, my dear brother," I mouth. "I can't."

He doesn't hear me anymore. He wheezes and suddenly exhales, as if to get rid of every last molecule of air in his lungs. Then, counterintuitively, he draws in wisps of air through his flaring nostrils and his open mouth all at once, trying to remember how to breathe.

I know he is doing everything he can to keep quiet, maybe as a last image of fortitude or dignity. A last attempt to feign bravery. But he cannot suppress the sharp cries of pain that escape him at every inhale, nor can he cover up his weakening heart with each exhale that drains the remaining life out of him, ounce by ounce.

He clasps my arm, feebly clawing at my chest holding onto dear life, clinging on to me with all his strength. As he draws his last breath, I caress his forehead.

Everything stands still and silent as his eyes flutter shut.

This place did not deserve you, *lala jan*. You can rest in peace now. You are in God's hands.

The sun is setting in the horizon, and his face gleams a shimmery bronze in the pale light. So calm and peaceful.

He is finally free.

For reasons I cannot understand, I give his already limp shoulders one final squeeze, and I refuse to let go. And even when the paramedics come to pry my hands off his lifeless body, I still refuse to let go.

Tired and tired of persecution
My Land
Without song and without sound
My Land
Painful and incurable
Sarzamine man.

3.7 Abe

I wait for Shahgul in our usual spot, at a corner behind one of the fruit and vegetable stalls in the *Jungle*. She messaged me to meet her here in the morning, but she is late. I haven't seen much of her or the children since the fight last week. We have been speaking on the phone though, and she said she was fine – I need to see it for myself.

Another boy died in that fight. Stabbed in the chest during the fight. Others got injured. Blood spurting out of arms and legs, wounds on heads, broken limbs, black eyes. It's a war zone in this camp. I keep telling the authorities we will not stand for it,that they need to send people away. We can't keep allowing our children to get killed in this place.

I glance down at my phone: 2:45 pm. I have been waiting for almost an hour and she is not here yet. It might be nothing. Maybe she has been held up by one of her chatty neighbours. That Kareema is a gossip and is probably asking her thousands of questions about where she disappears to every time she meets with me.

There has been a lot of talk about us in the camp lately. A single mother going around with the young community representative is a hot topic for all of the Afghans. That's one other aspect of our culture I shun and was hoping I could get away from. For now, I have reluctantly agreed to be more careful when being seen together in public. Not for myself, I couldn't care less what people say or think. But I'd do anything to protect Shahgul and the kids from those vipers' tongues.

Aside from everything else that has happened, I received my red stamp this morning. I am not allowed to leave the island under any circumstances. All because someone up in the hierarchy decided I am not vulnerable enough to deserve their sympathy.

An entire system has been devised where refugees teach each other to employ the most extreme measures to prove they are vulnerable, and therefore earn their *vulnerability status*, which in turn gets them the blue stamp. That is the only way we can leave this island legally, by being considered, in the eyes of the authorities, as *vulnerable*. *Vulnerable* like having a terminal disease or disability or something drastic which would theoretically justify the fact that we cannot live in the squalid conditions of Moria indefinitely. Never mind that no human being can.

Growing up in Iran meant being permanently labelled a foreigner in all aspects of life. The work there was so unstable for Afghans, as was the pay. Sometimes I would work endless hours for several months and not get a cent in return. But at least in Iran, I had a roof over my head. I had family and relatives to help me through hard times, and they lived just a few blocks away. I had an income, however meagre or unreliable.

Then, when the recession in Iran deepened, Afghans became the first to bear the brunt of US sanctions. The first to be let go from their jobs. The first to be evicted. The first whose marginalised lives became more expendable. I had no choice but to leave.

During my childhood, I spent all my spare time watching foreign movies, so I was already semi-fluent in English. I heaved whatever of my belongings I could carry over my shoulders and, the first chance I got, I followed an influx of straggling refugees into this other world.

My mother had every hope that I would come to Europe,

get a job within weeks, and send some money home every now and then.

She had caressed my face with her prematurely pruney hands and planted a kiss on my forehead.

"If anyone can rise above this *nothing* life, *bachem,* it is you."

My mother was wrong about me. If I was nothing in Iran, I am even less than nothing in Moria – I am likely to remain that way.

I glimpse my phone. Shahgul is not here yet, and that probably means she will not show up. I am just about to get up and leave, when she finally appears with Frishta and Mohsen on either side of her, all dressed up.

Frishta is wearing a lovely yellow dress, her cinnamon, shoulder-length hair is made into a tight braid. Mohsen fidgets uncomfortably in a white buttoned-up dress shirt and beige chino shorts. And then there is Shagul. She is all made up, cherry lip-gloss covering up the chaps on her full lips. Her pink, satin head scarf frames her round face, with strands of caramel brown hair poking through casually. She looks absolutely stunning.

But her voice is stiff; I feel as if I am shrinking as she instructs the children to stay put while she beckons me to an even more secluded corner. With her head bowed low, and with a mix of elation and sadness, she murmurs that their ticket to Athens has arrived and that they are leaving.

She waits for my cue. When I remain silent, she throws herself into my arms and bawls, with no regard for what people may say or think.

"Abolfazl."

There she goes, calling my cursed birth name again with her silky voice, churning the ground beneath me into butter.

She doesn't want to leave me, she cries, but she cannot allow her children to grow up in a place like this.

"You understand, don't you?" She pleads.

I lay her head gently on my shoulder and stroke her cheek, trying to memorise its warm, velvety texture before it fades away. She tilts her chin up, her eyes begging for my sadness or anger, or whatever I can give her. But my lips are pressed together in silent rumination. I refuse to show any reaction, because I know full well that if I do, even more tears will come streaming down her tinted cheeks. I don't want to be the reason for her crying.

I tell her I am happy for her, even though that is a lie. I tell her we both knew this moment would come, even though I have been living in a bubble of denial for longer than I can remember. So long, that I have forgotten how to tell it apart from reality. I tell her she has to go, to move on with her life, for her sake and for her children's sake, even though I know for certain there is no one on this Earth who would make them as happy as I would. I tell her they are too good for this place, that Moria never deserved them, even though I would much rather that she stays. As selfish as it may be, I would rather we rot together than rotting here on my own.

But here is the thing about refugees; some get to move on, while others can never shake themselves free from the shackles. What we all have in common, though, is that displacement is in our blood. We can never let ourselves get attached to anything. The glimmer of happiness we may have thought to have achieved will come crashing down on us, one way or another.

I don't tell her that she changed me. Nor that I will never let myself make the mistake of loving another again. Instead, I clasp onto her so tightly, with my fingers only barely grazing hers, and my lips heavy with words unsaid.

Minutes slip into hours, maybe even days. Perhaps the bus is late, or perhaps it is the eternity of goodbye that makes time stand still. I hold her and she holds me, unyielding, while everything else becomes motionless and insignificant.

This is the image of her I want to cling onto before beginning to doubt whether she is a real person who I have actually loved, or whether she is the embodiment of a homeland that I have dissociated myself from. Perhaps she is both.

Eventually, I will grow to understand that memories cannot be trusted. Memories are attachments to the past; they give a sense of false belonging. A history. An identity. For refugees, memories should be banished and attachments should be severed because you never know when you will have to let go. You never know when your life might change again. You never know when you will be called on again and asked to give up everything you know and move into the unknown.

When people start flocking next to the main road, anticipating their onward journey, all wearing their best clothes with their life's belongings stuffed into plastic bags and burlap sacks, we know it is time.

"I love you, Shahgul," I say to her simply. "Did you know that?"

She nods a fervent yes. Of course she knows.

She cups my burning cheeks in her velvet hands as I wipe her face clean of her tears with mine. Mohsen runs into my arms, sobbing loudly enough for the whole crowd of passengers to hear. Frishta wraps her arms around me next and plants a gentle kiss on my cheek, her eyes despondent and watery.

"*Khoda hafez, kaka* Abolfazl," she whispers softly into my ear, swallowing back the sob in her throat.

"Goodbye, my angel, my little Frishta," I murmur back.

And then, I let them go. Just as I have been trained to do. Just as every refugee is trained to do.

They hop on to the bus and Shahgul gives me one final radiating beam in between her tears. Then she spins around and disappears. And so does Abolfazl.

STAGE 4: DEPRESSION

*When the terminally ill patient can no longer
deny his illness, when he is forced to undergo more
surgery or hospitalisation, when he begins to have
more symptoms or becomes weaker and thinner,
he cannot smile it off anymore. His numbness or
stoicism, his anger and rage will soon be replaced
with a sense of great loss.*[5]

Elisabeth Kübler-Ross

---

5   Kubler-Ross, Elisabeth. *On Death and Dying: What the Dying Have to Teach Doctors, Nurses, Clergy and Their Own Families.* Scribner, 2014.

4.1 Mahdi

My therapist is composed, mild-mannered and always makes sure to speak in a low, soothing tone.

"How are you feeling this week, Mahdi?" she asks, gaze firmly on her notepad.

She probably cares about my well-being, as much as her professional licence allows her to. And yet I still can't help but wonder if it is justified that any person should dedicate their life's work to reducing all the moments I have ever lived to a few rushed squiggles on a notepad.

She peers at me through her thin-framed glasses, appraising me with her eyes. She wants me to say something. Probably something about my best friend, Jawed. About what his life did for me, or what his death did to me. Or maybe this week she wants me to unravel more of my past, delve deeper into detail about my self-proclaimed *God-loving* death squad back in Afghanistan. Maybe she wants to know why I still haven't tried to call my mother after all this time.–

I let my eyes shift around, taking in the bareness of her cold, sterile office. Just a caravan with a makeshift desk and a couple of chairs. This is one of the only other places I see, other than the darkness under my covers that I pull tightly over my face day and night.

I am forced to come here every week by *Section B's* managers, but I don't see the point. It's not that the therapist is not nice or professional enough. It's not that she is not good at what she does. But I was never much of a talker anyway and I don't really see how starting now is likely to help me shed the monotony that has taken over my life.

I absently take a cigarette out of the pack in my pocket and place it in my mouth. Then, seeing the disapproving look on her face, I take it out of my mouth, put it back in the pack, and stare down at my feet.

"Hey, hey," she coos sympathetically as I raise my head.

I must have started crying again without realising it. It happens so often, I can't even tell the difference anymore.

She pulls out a tissue from her vest pocket and dabs my face gently. I don't tell her that I prefer the moistness. Or that, as much as I appreciate the gesture, her hand is like pins and needles. It invades my skin and deprives me of the only remaining evidence that my emotions still exist.

There may have been a point when I convinced myself that if I cry while telling others my story, it would stop having such a hold on me; like a sport that just needs some practice before getting to grips with. But the story's details change every time; my memory plays tricks on me and I begin to forget which part was real and which was a fabrication of my overactive imagination. And then there are moments, though important, that I never want to talk about. Not ever.

"Your father—" she begins.

I hold up my hand. No. Not him. I will not talk about him.

She nods sympathetically, then tells me that I do not need to answer any questions I don't feel ready to answer. But then she goes on to ask those very questions that make me relapse into the thoughts I come here to erase. Those moments are so fossilised in my memories, like relics of the past to be put on display.

What my therapist doesn't know is that even something as harmless as asking me how I am feeling has the potential to trigger me. Something as harmless as asking me what I did this week can slingshot me back into that restricted place that I am trying to shut out.

So I just sit in silence and stare vacantly into the void.

"Are you getting out enough? Why don't you go for a walk? Get some fresh air?" she suggests, her mouth a faint line curving upwards. Just like Jawed's used to.

I can't go for walks. Anxiety imprisons me in my room, where I lie on the bed for hours waiting, just waiting for something; anything. Like another execution waiting to happen – this time, hopefully mine.

Most people think the worst part of an impending execution is the pain that comes with severing the head from the body. But that is only momentary. The worst part is that time spent waiting; that time between when the execution order is received, and when it actually happens. The waiting is always the worst part. That is what Moria is: – the time between the announcement of a death sentence and its completion.

"Keep yourself busy. Just find a way to pass the time to take your mind off things."

I tried chatting to the other kids, volunteering in the *section*, trying to help others like me to forget about life for a while. But what is the point when I see Jawed in every single one of them? What if I fail to protect them too, just like I failed to protect him? I have tried to play the part of a survivor, when I know full well that it has no place here. Instead, I'd rather shut myself away from the world so I can cry freely until my eyes refuse to make any more tears.

"You look tired. Are you getting enough sleep?"

Sleep never comes; not in a restful way anyway. The nights hold me hostage and insomnia sweeps in to make sure I am fully awake for the cold, dead eyes that fixate on me. My scar blazes, even in my dreams.

Sleep does not offer me any escape; it is part and parcel of this recurring nightmare. The one about piercing screams just before an attack, or the pieces of raw flesh that carpet the earth just after an explosion. The one with glimpses of normality that shatter like broken glass when reality swoops in. The one about death in all its colours.

She leans in closer and brings her voice down to a murmur.

"Is it that you are afraid of dying?"

I conquered the fear of dying long ago, when I was forced to put my life in the hands of strangers. It is not the fear of death that cripples me, or the fear of pain that holds my thoughts captive. I used to feel pain when I was beaten to a pulp by the men in uniform for every minor disobedience. But even then, at least I could tell I was still alive.

What scares me is living between life and death. What scares me is this life that has trapped me, and what is the point of pretending to be alive for others when I am barely surviving? What scares me is not death itself, it is death here, in this unforgivable camp, where death goes unnoticed, where it is forgotten the next day, just like Jawed's was.

My teeth begin to chatter. They have started doing that lately, and there are times I can't make them stop for hours.

I ask her what is happening to me. She says she has seen this before. A trauma resurfacing. Symptoms can take months – even years – to show up.

"It is very common among refugees," she concludes. "Because of what happened to you in your country."

"Because of what happened in *my* country?" I ask, looking her in the eyes for the first time in weeks.

I surprise myself when I throw my head back and laugh. But what comes out is not a laugh at all, but a bitter, unnatural choking.

"You must really not know what is happening in *yours*."

We remain silent as the therapist finishes scribbling down her notes and closes her pad.

"Time's up. See you next week?"

Maybe. If I can tear myself away from my inner world and guarantee my soul safe passage through the crowds of hollow bodies and sunken faces. If I can bear the cadences of humming chests and discordant heartbeats that make up a morbid composition for the dejected. But above all, if I can convince myself to ignore the voice in my head that reminds me, only when it has to, that it is so much easier to die lying face-down, than it is to stand up and walk.

4.2 Maryam

My first childhood memory is not a memory, but a dream.

I'm three or four, with a bobbed haircut and a perfectly straight fringe; standing on a balcony in our apartment in Tehran, gazing out into the horizon. I peer at the bright orange sky for seconds that feel like minutes, and minutes that feel like hours, searching, probing, despondently pursuing an ever fleeting peace; a sense of calm that, for whatever reason, refuses to have anything to do with me.

A snow-white dove fllies towards me in all its splendour, and perches on the railing next to me.

"Be patient," the dove murmurs. Not with words, but with its radiating presence. "Peace will be yours one day."

And just like that, I feel at ease.

Even when the bird leaves me and glides off into the sunrise, even then, I relish in the enlightened aura it has left behind.

There were things I never understood about my country, even as a child. Like why, in school, children were made to trample on the flags of enemy countries before starting class. Or why in assemblies, we were made to sing songs that aggrandised martyrs and made us wish for similar fates of bloodshed and death. Or why anyone who remembered its history in a positive light. or was opposed to anything the government ever did, dared never to speak out, else they should follow the same fate as all those other refugees, fleeing their homeland in search for freedom of expression.

Mine was a nation that knew how to keep its defences up, lest foreign invaders tried to do to it what they had been doing for decades to neighbouring countries like Afghanistan. Mine was a nation that knew how to cultivate a military mindset from a young age in its new generations, training them to wish to die a glorious demise for its flag, long before we were old enough to understand the repercussions of that wish.

For months, maybe even years, the white dove visited me in my sleep and showered me with millions of molecules of hope that seeped through my bloodstream and wedged themselves deep into my heart. That was when I was still living in Tehran.

When I moved to Europe, I thought the dove had abandoned me for good. I assumed that it was because I didn't need her presence anymore; I believed I had finally found my peace.

After more than 20 years, the dove has come to me again. This time, she looks different. She is no longer that motivating, energising being that wordlessly reassured my four-year-old self; she no longer radiates promises of serenity or bliss. My dove wobbles on the railing, her tired eyes pleading with mine. In the distance, an invisible ticking counts down her seconds – they are running out.

I wake up with a start to the sound of my phone buzzing. I glance at the screen reluctantly through my heavy lids to view the message I have been dreading.

"ALL NGO STAFF TO STAY AT HOME UNTIL FURTHER NOTICE."

It has been several days since supporters of the Golden Dawn, far-right party in Greece, have been mobilising in Lesbos. Just last week, they attacked a colleague of mine with sticks and stones and vandalised his car. They have also reportedly attacked refugees, journalists and local anti-fascist residents on separate occasions allegedly set fire to one of our community centres.

Since President Erdogan threatened to *"open Turkey's gates"* to Europe, letting hundreds more asylum seekers to cross the sea into Lesbos, even more neo-Nazis have found the courage to crawl out of their ditches and into the light – and not just in Lesbos or Greece. Rumours have been circulating, that white supremacists have been flying in to stand with their far-right brothers and sisters in arms to defend their twisted version of Europe.

Tensions have been building up in other ways too. Just this morning, Athens decided to ship in hundreds of riot police officers to construct a closed detention centre to replace Moria. It is a plan the government has been breaking in for months, to contain the thousands of asylum seekers who are meant to be shipped back to Turkey as per the EU-Turkey agreement. In practice, a closed centre would mean more restrictions, more controlled movements, and a lower likelihood for more refugees to cross over into Europe. Local people and aid workers are furious at the prospect.

In all of this, our organisation's response is to keep staff members out of harm's way. I understand no one wants to be legally accountable for their staff meeting some tragic fate. But keeping us contained doesn't solve anything. It sends a wrong message to the world and tells the fascists exactly what they want to hear.

Chamberlain's policy of appeasement didn't help Europe during World War II, and it is not about to start making the world a better place now. To lie down in silence means relinquishing any claim we may have to this island and its people. The sheer thought of it makes me feel sick.

I snatch my phone back in a haze, and type furiously into the group chat. *There must be something we can do.*

A few minutes pass before my phone buzzes again.

Not getting yourself hurt. That's something.

I text Yusif instead. If anyone is going to find some way to stand up for what is right, it is him.

Where are you?

A few seconds later, my phone buzzes again. No words, just a snapshot of a roadblock. Hundreds of riot police, having just disembarked, are being blocked by hundreds of volunteers, refugees and sympathetic local residents.

The angle of the photo suggests Yusif is right in the middle of the crowd. Local residents, anti-fascists, refugees and NGO staff who oppose the construction of this new prison are there, waving their arms in the air, eyes fearless, demeanour resolute, taking back control of their island.

A ghost of a smile appears on my face. I didn't expect any less from Yusif. I text back hurriedly, as I jump out of bed, dress and rush out into the night.

I'll be there in 10.

I trek all the way to the port where the standoff between the protesters and the police is meant to be happening. I can discern a few police officers from a distance, but I don't see any crowds of protesters standing their ground.

Something feels eerie; the air is heavy with imminent chaos – a ticking time bomb.

As I draw nearer, an acrid stench invades my lungs and throat. I start coughing in fits to expunge the invading force. *Tear gas.* Though I knew they had used it on refugees in the past, I had never known them to use it against their own people.

Through watery eyes, I find some dispersed protesters, running away in a frenzy, some crying, some coughing and others covering their face with their sleeves. Humanitarian workers and local people are running away, running for their lives, their resolute expressions now replaced by uncertainty and fear. And this time, they are not running from white supremacists or neo-fascists, not from a niche community of deluded individuals, but from their very own government.

Something about this scene is reminiscent of the way protests are dealt with in my country. The protests that are quashed by police brutality. The way protesters are silenced through any means necessary, and sometimes, never again seen. Except, this time the scene is unfolding in our esteemed Europe. The self-proclaimed gatekeeper of human rights. The birthplace of democracy itself.

A police officer yells out into the smoke as he makes his way back to the ship.

"You will beg us to return."

I gaze through the smog, at the bittersweet victory of what remains of the protesters; muted and horror-struck, my chest constricted and my breathing became shallow.

Then something strange happens to me. It is the oddest sensation, as if something in me finally breaks: an elastic band that had been stretched out for too long, finally snaps.

I am not sad, nor angry, nor confused by the severe injustice that has just unfolded before me. I can no longer be moved nor surprised nor shocked by anything that unfolds hereafter. Nor do I feel the urge to ever shed another tear.

Instead, I find myself transported back to that same balcony on the 10th floor, taking in the familiar view of Tehran. Once again, I am a child yearning for peace; this time not just for myself but for every person who needs to be rescued from this island.

My dove must hear my calls, as, before I know it, the shadow of a ghost looms in the horizon.

She is bloodied all over. Her beak chipped, her right wing

broken. She falters in mid-air and falls out of the sky, right into my arms. She looks like she is coming straight out of war.

"Why?" I gasp.

She shakes her head with what little might she has left, eyes blinking frantically. She is trying to tell me something, but before she can, her body begins to convulse. Her good wing thrashes as she desperately pants for air.

My face hardens. My little hands gain a life of their own as they clasp her throat and begin to squeeze. Then, my four-year-old self stands back and watches as the life drains out of the dove.

4.3 Abe

"Sir?" the reporter glances at me, her daunting blue eyes shifting with uncertainty.

I cannot make sense of her speech immediately. The word falls out of her mouth like lead. It sounds warped, as if it was first spoken underground, and is now trying to reach the surface.

There's a tentative look in her eyes when I gaze back at her, the kind of look Shahgul used to have whenever she caught me lost in thought or rumination. It is a look that suggests I have zoned out again. It happens so often lately. I am so very tired of fighting everyone's battles for them; I am tired of telling everyone's story to anyone who will listen and having it fall on deaf ears. So now I just surrender to apathy.

"Are you ready?" the reporter inquires, it seems, not for the first time. This time, the words come through more clearly.

The reporter is a pale, scrawny woman in her early forties, with her silver blond hair done up in a tight bun. She says she represents one of the world's top media agencies with millions of viewers worldwide. As to where she is from, I am sure she mentioned the name of one of those Northern European countries I once had dreams of reaching with Shahgul and the kids.

It's been one and a half months since I last saw her. I haven't even spoken to her since the day she left. Shahgul has tried calling, but I freeze every time I see her name pop up on my phone screen. Instead, I wait for the ringing to slowly die out. I'm not proud of it but I know it has to be this way. I cannot let her see me so vacant and devoid of everything I once was. No longer the outspoken, caring man she claimed to love once upon a time.

She would not even recognise me anymore; I hardly recognise myself. Sleepless nights carve dark circles under my eyes; a loss of appetite pulls my skin tighter around my ribs. I feel like drowning every day and every day I feel I should let myself.

Before starting the interview, the reporter reminds me that if I should, at any point, feel like breaking down and weeping, I should not try to withhold it because viewers have a right to see the truth. I do not tell the reporter that I forgot how to cry long ago, and even if I still remembered, I would save my tears for something more meaningful than a five-minute TV interview.

I wonder when it was, exactly, that I chose to step back and allow my suffering, the suffering of all the people in this camp, to be turned into a bite-sized story on migration for viewers to relate to. Perhaps as a representative, I am supposed to play the part of a hero, always putting my community's needs before my own . Or perhaps it is the story of love and loss they are after, the one about the broken hearted fool stuck forever in a refugee camp. I wonder when I decided to give up ownership of my life's story and allow for it to be turned into an inspiration for the collective; why this farce should make the slightest difference in what remains of a life that is still my own.

"Sir, are you ready?" the reporter says again, this time more impatiently.

I cannot blame her. I am wasting her time. The channel probably has other asylum seekers to interview today, and the women and children with disabilities are bound to break more hearts and get higher ratings than a suffering man in his early 20s.

I nod simply, as the cameraman guides me through a

countdown with his fingers.

5... I sit up in my chair, looking slightly more alert than before; 4... I take a deep breath in and let it out in a sigh; 3... I lean forward with my torso, as per the reporter's instructions, to provide a clearer view of my surroundings. I am sitting right at the front of an open tent to show the compact space inside; 2... I open my eyes to conceal their vacancy; 1... I gaze straight into the camera, ready to transform into that quintessential refugee the world wants to see.

And the film is rolling.

"We are on the island of Lesbos, Greece, in Moria refugee camp," the reporter begins in her on-camera voice. "Where recent attacks on refugees and volunteers have been reported. The camp is built for a capacity of 3,000 and now houses more than 20,000 asylum seekers. It has been called *'the worst refugee camp in the world'* by its residents and by other news channels. Having been refused a permit to enter the camp proper, we are coming to you now from the sub-camp right next to Moria, a place nicknamed the *Olive Grove* or the *Jungle*, where thousands of men, women and children are forced to share a single, defective water outlet..."

I stop listening again. The reporter's words begin to dissolve into the background, and then they drown into a soundless monotony, as everyone's speech does for me lately. I am transported once again to that place of delirium. That place that beckons me to stop wading through the quicksand and let it devour my entire body, mind and soul.

When I re-emerge from my trance, I find the reporter peering at me sternly, her eyes twitching.

Then she demandsthat I share my story with the globe. So I brace myself and say, in my rehearsed English, that I no longer have a story that belongs to me personally. It became fused with thousands of others' the day I stepped into this refugee camp. I might have had one once, but now my only story is that of the collective –of Moria.

"So, tell us," the reporter prompts eagerly.

I go through the usual drill. The inedible food. The squalid living conditions. Absence of decent medical care. Lack of dignity and human rights.

"Children are dying," I say. "Women are being raped. We are all being attacked by extremist groups. And no one seems to give a damn."

The reporter nods her head vigorously, infused with on-screen compassion as I tick off her speaking points, one by one. A checklist that has become so commonplace it now lacks any real meaning.

I am stuck on this one tune on a broken record with its beats pulsating like coronary spasms, losing all connection with the melody it may have once produced. I have heard somewhere that if you repeat something frequently enough, it loses its integrity. Maybe that works with people too.

When I approach the end of my speech, the reporter adjusts her clip-on microphone and, almost as an afterthought, poses a final question.

"Is there anything else you would like to share with our viewers?"

I consider the question for a moment. Not because I haven't been asked it before, but because for the first time in weeks, there is an independent thought brewing in my mind; something that feels so foreign to me, that I choose to indulge it.

"Someone once told me,", . This is not what I have rehearsed. "That becoming a refugee is like being obliterated from the face of the Earth. Like that little five-year-old boy, who burned to death in the recent fire. The authorities insisted that he never existed in the first place. Or the teenager, who was stabbed to death in a fight a few weeks back, and never mentioned since. They can erase us because our lives, refugee lives, don't matter to these people."

I pause to consider my next words.

"But I don't think that even that kind of statement really captures the severity of what it is to be a refugee. Becoming a refugee is more like having the air you breathe sucked out of your lungs, so gradually and painfully, that when you finally start to suffocate, you thank God for it. Because then, at least, when you come to the verge of death, for one fleeting instant, you matter. Even if they lose no time in making an example of you in the press the next morning, and forget you ever existed the next evening. Even if you are only alive to relish it for one split second, at least just for that moment, you can say that you became someone again. At least for that one moment, you stop being part of this collective narrative that news anchors and reporters insist on showcasing to the world, and you remember what it is like to be an individual."

The reporter is quiet, unfazed; her lips part expectantly, waiting for my cue. But I have nothing more to say. I am done putting myself out there. I am done being made an example of. So, I stop, and embrace the dazed stillness I am used to.

I tilt my head back slightly, and let my eyes soften. I drown out the lights and the noise of the raving TV crew, and I settle back into apathy. I find a strange sort of relief in my loneliness and vacancy. I feel untouchable here, like I am always welcome in the deepest, darkest corners of my mind. Where nothing stirs, no sounds or images and no one else is allowed in.

4.4 Maryam

Extract from Maryam's Diary, 19 October 2019

There is something I need to tell you. I don't even know how to begin. The truth is, I'm not who you think I am. Or who I thought I was, for that matter. It's all a pretence, a front; a lie I got so used to telling, I can no longer tell the difference between what's real and what's not.

It's hard to describe Moria to someone who hasn't been there. When I tell people what I do for a living, they ooh and aah. When I tell them about the scenes of violence, misery and rape, that happen daily in their very own Europe, they gasp and shake their heads. When I tell them even humanitarian workers can become targets of hatred, not just for demented fascists and riot police, but even for refugees themselves, they act stunned.

They've seen it on the news. They've heard about the conditions there. They don't understand how I can keep going back.

I get patted on the back. Lauded for my courage. Told the world needs more people like me.

The truth is this. Every morning I wake up and dab water on my face, then I put on my makeup, painting myself in bright colours; but not too bright, in case I offend the patients. It's Moria, after all. Like going to a funeral, you don't want to stand out too much.

I don't like mirrors. I try to avoid them but when I have no other choice I see sullied skin where there used to be warmth. Indentations where there used to be elasticity. Shadows where there used to be light. I paint over my face; every inch, every corner, erasing every trace of my selfhood. I don't my vest, secure my badge to my lapel and step into the van, all smiles and waves, ready for another day of Moria.

To arrive at the clinic is to feel nauseated. To hear mothers complain about their kids' cough or rash for the hundredth time prompts sighs and discrete eye rolls. Even to hear a child cry or walk around barefoot on dirt and mud triggers nothing. Not anymore.

I am void. The unthinkable has happened.

Moria has become the new normal.

Eventually, holding back tears of anger and indignation becomes tedious. Then, so does crying. There are times even breathing becomes a burden.

Some nights, I lie awake for hours, thinking nothing; dreaming nothing. Other nights, I catch myself googling the most painless ways to kill myself.

I admire people who go out on a limb to make a dramatic exit from the world. Working with refugees for so many years, I have come to learn a number of ways to commit suicide, from wrapping discarded cables around your throat, to slashing wrists, or even setting yourself on fire. As for me, all of that seems a bit too out there and not in line with my introverted nature. I'd much rather something subtler, like a quiet overdose or self-inflicted hypothermia. Even in death, I am not as courageous as people make me out to be.

It is not that I feel dejected or unhappy. I could deal with that. It is that I have ceased to feel. I am vacant, completely numb. Like there is a gaping hole, drilling its way deeper into my heart's centre at the end of every working day and I can feel it growing larger every night.

My bedroom is my only refuge. Moonlight ripples in through the drapes, breathing life into austere contours and shapes that lie around me. My backpack covered in layers of soot from a day's work in the camp, my vest draping lifelessly over the chair in the corner, my badge identifying me as a humanitarian, as someone whose job it is to care.

There is an old folk song I used to sing during long car

rides with my parents in Iran. Back then, I thought it was a love sonnet that tells the story of a man who is so desperately in love with his sweet Maryam, that he lies awake all night thinking about her. I wished, one day, to be that Maryam for someone. I wished for someone to dream of seeing me in their waking hours and all throughout the night, through thoughts and fantasies of their own.

Baaz dobareh sobh shod, man hanooz bidaram,
It's morning again and I'm still awake

Kaash mikhabidam, toro khaab mididam,
I wish I could sleep and see you in my dreams

But now I hear the tune in the back of my mind, and I hear the words in a different light. It's like the man is mourning a loss; something unreal, an image, a fantasy conjured up by his imagination. It's like that Maryam never even existed. She is something he made up in a moment of desperation to tell the world he is not so alone. To tell people he used to be somebody, even though that only ever meant existing in her imaginary shadow.

Khoosheye gham tooye delam, zade javoone doone be doone,
Seeds of sorrow flourished in my heart

Del nemidoone, che kone ba in gham?
How does the heart handle this pain?

Ay, nazanine Maryam
Oh, sweet Maryam

I lie awake wondering if that voice is mine. Did that image of my childhood self singing in the car ever exist in the real world? Or is it something my imagination made up to make me feel whole? To hide the empty vessel that I have become society's fabrication – painted all over, feigning compassion, feigning feeling – when I know there is nothing genuine left in my heart?

Is this what Moria does to people? Erase every last trace of their past selves, deplete every last ounce of humanity, and leave them completely hollow?

I wonder if people in Moria lie awake at night, wondering the same.

4.5 Zarifa

My son,

When you open your eyes and spot the despondent gaze staring back at you, you will ask me why we are here. Then, you will see the tattered blankets – or what remains of them – wrapped loosely around your fragile body and your tiny nose will pick up whiffs of the acrid sewage festering around you. And when you begin to hear the eruption of yelling and relentless words in dialects of Arabic and Farsi, whose meanings you will not recognise for a long time to come, you will ask what this place is and why you were born here.

I will tell you that we had no other choice but to come here. That we had enemies at home who would have killed us if we hadn't risked our lives and crossed borders into countries unknown and then across the stony sea. That it might not seem like it now but this refugee camp is actually the safest place for us and that, one day, you will thank me for bringing you here.

You might believe me at first. For a couple of years, you might even love me for it, but soon you will start to learn how to tell when your mother is lying. When she gets that twitch in her left eyebrow, you will know she is not telling the full truth. But if you knew the truth, you might hate me even more .

Would you believe me if I told you that I would rather you weren't born at all? If I told you I believed your eyes were too chaste to shed a tear, and your lips too honest to stifle a sob in a place as cruel as Moria? If I told you I would rather have your mouth run dry than have you taste a drop of its water, that I would rather have you starve than let your stomach take a crumb of its food, that I would rather have you never blink an eye or watch you toss and turn all night, than catch a wink of sleep in this place? – What would you say? Would the truth sound better then?

It is not that I don't want my children to ever be challenged. I am not the kind of mother who would shelter her children from all the hardships of life. I want you to be a fighter just like your *baba* was before you. You never met your father, but he was a good man; a great man. He fought hard for us and he did everything so we could have a decent life back home. He worked two, sometimes three jobs just to put food on the table at least once a day, and if ever there was a day where he couldn't, he would not come home at all for the shame of facing his family.

He spent his whole life fighting for me, for us, and he even died fighting. He was truly a hero. Or at least, I will tell you that was your father, but again, my eyebrow would twitch and my teeth would clench l, and then you would know that I am lying.

Would it be better if I told you that the man I married did unspeakable things to your mother and to your older brother, Milad? That he even threatened to kill him? That it was his hatred and loathing that drove me and your siblings to a life of exile? But he was not your father either; he could not have been.

Would it be better if I told you I don't even know who your father is? That he is probably one of the three men who assaulted me, in the fields behind this very camp, in broad daylight? If it was, at least I hope it was the one with the repenting eyes. I don't know if he really regretted what he did to me –what they surely do to all women who are desperate enough to be here without their husband's protection– but at a moment where I feel so hopeless as to search for a shred of humanity in others, I am forced to flail my hands in this vast vacuum of nothingness and take whatever I can get.

I don't want to tell you what I had to endure to keep my children alive. I don't want to tell you how I thought coming here would mean giving you all a better life, that I was so naive to believe those intolerable days I put my son through were all behind me. I don't want to have to tell you that every day, the distance between your brother and I grows bigger; that I am losing him in the void of his own depression and that I know now that everything I have suffered has been for nothing.

I want to be able to tell you that Europe is a place worth fighting for, and I want you to believe me when I do. I want to tell you that we will leave Moria soon, that a better life is waiting for us in Europe. The real Europe, the one everyone always speaks so highly of. I want to tell you that without my eyebrow twitching. Without my teeth grinding together like abrasive iron manacles. I want to be able to tell you that your future is bright without breaking down and crying.

But as long as your birthplace is Moria, you would know that I'm lying. No good comes from telling the truth here anyway. Any glimmer of hope one might have is rooted in the lies this place was built on. The lies we told ourselves when we came here. The lies we keep telling ourselves while we are still here, and the lies we will tell ourselves if we ever leave this place. But lying to myself is one thing; lying to you is something I could never bear.

That is why I would rather end your life before it begins. Because I am certain you would agree with me that being born here is an end at the very beginning; that the Europe we speak of is not worth spending a single day in this place for; that living a lie, is not really living at all.

I hope you will understand that I do this not because I don't care about you. I hope you understand that, if there is one truth you will ever hear from me, it is this: I love you.

With love from Moria,

Your Mother,
Zarifa

4.6 Maryam

When I first meet him, I am on the verge of breaking.

They warn you not to get in too deep when you begin your career as a humanitarian aid worker. They warn you that what you may witness will be out of the breadth of normal human experience. That, though you may have heard about it in news reports, films, books or documentaries, it is an entirely different experience to see it first-hand and that if you choose to walk away at any point, no one would judge you.

Burn-out. Compassion fatigue. Vicarious trauma. Secondary or acute stress. Self-care. They throw these buzzwords in your face when you embark on humanitarian life, and you never really begin to appreciate them until it hits you. Because it will hit you, one way or another. And once it does, you will never be the same again.

Even if you step away from it all. Even if you take that much needed rest, or that leave of absence, or *rest and recovery leave -* call it what you want. They are all just fancy ways to shroud the reality of your degenerating state of mind. You are experiencing traumatic stress. Symptoms might be mild or severe, they vary from person to person. Your experiences from the past may colour what you are witnessing in the present, or they might not. But stay working in the field long enough, and you will probably collapse into some form of depression.

You begin to crumble, day by day and the worst part is that nobody sees it . Because you keep going. You keep a straight face and turn up for work, regardless of the utter collapse of your mind, and you push through with every cell in your being, counting down the hours until you can be away from prying eyes. Alone, you can stop hiding and let your inner darkness take over.

So, when I say that when I first meet him I am on the verge of breaking, what I actually mean to say is that I am already pushed way past my limits. I mean I am already in that state of depression; I just don't want to admit it yet. Not to myself, and certainly not to anybody else.

He walks up to me, a hemp bag dangling from his shoulder down to his waist. His swift, light gait highlighting a sense of purpose, and tells me, quite simply, that he's been tortured.

In the same voice that people utter a greeting or tell you their name for the first time, he tells me he's had a microchip planted in his brain. That he was a political prisoner in Iran, then in Turkey, and that he managed to escape somehow. But he is being tracked. Listened to. Even right now.

He whispers the last bit.

One way or another, I know he needs help. So I refer him to Mental Health Support teams. He is not interested.

"Don't you see," he pleads. "I need a surgeon to remove the tracking device."

I can't help him.

"There are no surgeons on this island that can help you," I say.

I have dismissed him but, without realising it, I have also given him something valuable that perhaps no one else has. I have seen him. Acknowledged him. Talked to him.

After that brief first encounter, he begins to seek me out every day. Sometimes with an excuse, sometimes without.

There are times I genuinely try to help him. He tells me he is being bullied in the camp, because he is confused about his gender and sexuality, and I try to support him in whatever way I can.

I provide information about *LGBT* support groups and

make sure they reach out to him. When he talks about his legal issues, I offer him information about legal services and where to find them. And just because I find it important enough, I keep suggesting that he reaches out for psychological support, which he still believes he does not need.

"It's not me, it is everyone else," he keeps reiterating. "They need to know what happened to me."

At some point, his constant presence in my life becomes draining. I try to explain that I have to work, that he has to stop coming to the clinic to see me every day. But he doesn't listen. So, one day, I snap.

"There is nothing more I can do for you. Stop bothering me!"

There was a point I could never have imagined myself saying this to another human being. Especially one with such a clear need for someone to care about him. But at this stage of my life, my compassion has run dry. I cannot even take care of myself anymore, let alone entertain the hopes of this deranged individual.

He leaves me alone.

For days, maybe weeks after that, I am left to focus on my own isolation. I cry every night. Some nights, I even jolt awake to shed more tears, because my subconscious has decided I have not suffered enough during daylight hours.

One day, when I am heading back from work, I see him again. Cars swish past him without a second a look – as do passersby – as he perches against a corner of the sidewalk. His tanned face clean-shaven, his hair unkempt. He is wearing the same coffee-stained T-shirt and khaki trousers and his trademark shoulder bag lays zipped-open by his side. He holds up a sign that reads, in shaky English letters:

I have been tortured.

Though I recognise him right away and empathise with his misery, I know for a fact that neither his hand-made sign nor his public display is going to get him very far. Simply because there is nothing special about him in a place like Moria. The majority of people in Moria have been tortured in one way or another. They just cannot or will not write it out for the whole world to see.

We lock eyes for a moment. His gaunt face betrays confusion and melancholy.

I am right here, it says. *Why can't they see me?*

Some people wear their depression on their sleeve. They paint themselves in austere colours of grey, black and other inky smudges for the whole world to see. Others would rather erase every last drop of its colour from their face when performing on the frontline. Then, only when the music stops, the crowds thin and the lights are off – only then do they give themselves permission to collapse into the abyss.

I drop my head low and hurry past him, like another unconcerned passerby, careful not to rekindle that misplaced glimmer of hope he identified in me before.

Eventually, I begin to heal. I make myself go to yoga classes every day after work and listen to meditation tracks every night before sleeping – it turns my world upside down. Yoga grounds me. It brings me into the present like never before, noticing everything around me. Meditation makes me confront my past self and accept who I was and who I have become. It retrieves me from the vacuum of my inner world. I learn to cultivate a sense of self-compassion, which had become so absent in my life. Day by day, as the negativity that controlled my mind begins to quieten down, I start to feel stronger.

* * * *

The next time I encounter him, he is lying right in the middle of an intersection on the road. Cars are honking, their vexed drivers are yelling, demanding angrily for him to get up. To stop being an obstacle. Even dying is considered a nuisance to some, if it disrupts their daily routine.

Pedestrians, who have stopped mid-track, are gathered in a circle around him. They keep a safe distance, enough to understand what is happening but not wanting to risk getting too close or involved.

I run towards him.

He is dead. It was me; I did this. I was his last hope. I ignored him, and now he is dead.

As I push past the crowds and draw closer, I notice his diaphragm expanding and contracting with every breath.

"*Chi shode?* What's wrong?" I drop down to my knees next to him. "Are you hurt?"

He blinks his eyes open, as if waking up from a deep sleep, and squints at me for a few seconds. I can tell he recognises me the moment his expression brightens. He smiles faintly and lifts his chin slightly. Then his gaze shifts directly behind me.

"Look," he says simply, his skinny finger pointing crookedly at the rows of cars his body is holding up. "They can finally see me."

STAGE 5: ACCEPTANCE

This stage is about accepting the reality [...] and recognising that this new reality is the permanent reality. We will never like this reality or make it OK, but eventually we accept it. We learn to live with it. It is the new norm with which we must learn to live. [...] Instead of denying our feelings, we listen to our needs; we move, we change, we grow, we evolve. We may start to reach out to others and become involved in their lives. We invest in our friendships and in our relationship with ourselves. We begin to live again, but we cannot do so until we have given grief its time.[6]

David Kessler

---

6   https://Grief.com/the-Five-Stages-of-Grief/.

5.1 Frishta

We are now settled in a refugee camp called Rafina, just outside of Athens. It is a small camp for women and children, home to around 16 families - half of them Afghan, the other half Syrian. We share a small room with another Afghan family, *khala* Tayeba and her twin sons, Ali and Reza, who are about the same age as Mohsen.

Khala Tayeba is often away, so Mummy and I end up looking after the boys most of the time. At first, we thought it would be nice for Mohsen to have them around to play with, but that was before we realised just how naughty Ali and Reza truly are. When they are not climbing over walls or throwing rocks at each other for fun, they're playing tricks on my poor little brother. Once, they tried feeding Mohsen worms telling him it was a secret Greek food only special boys could eat – good thing I slapped it out of his hand in time.

Luckily, lately the family has not been home much, so we mostly have the room to ourselves. They only come back for a few days per month to get their cash cards topped up, and then they leave again. No one knows for sure where they go, but some say they are trying to smuggle out of the country and make their way to Germany.

The day we left Moria, Mummy cried for the whole bus and ferry ride to Athens. She didn't even try to hide it, like she used to before. Mohsen kept tugging at her shirt, in his own little way telling her it was okay. I wanted to tell her that too, but Mummy taught me never to tell a lie. It's not okay. Nothing is okay.

In many ways Rafina is better than Moria. There are less

people, it is much calmer; and most importantly it is much safer. The only thing the boys fight about here is who is the best footballer in the world. Why do boys take football so seriously? They got into an actual fist fight because Elias said Messi was the best, and Benyamin insisted it was Ronaldo. Then their mothers came out and dragged them back into their rooms by the ear, and that was the end of that.

Rafina is much better than Moria in many ways. But even I am not too small to understand that when we received our tickets to Athens and got all excited, thinking we were finally ready to move on with our lives, another refugee camp was not what we were expecting.

Moria had its problems, but at least we had our friends and neighbours. We had *kaka* Abolfazl, who was more like a dad to me than my actual *baba*, the great abandoner. And even though she has stopped crying now, I know how much Mummy misses him deep down, and how much she wishes he were here.

There was also *khala* Kareema and *khala* Zarifa. My best friends Elaha and Arezoo. And then Abbas. My chest feels tight as I remember the last time I saw him, and how he ran headfirst into the angry mob of fighters. I try to shake the image away. Every time I think of him, I feel so sad I want to break down and cry for hours

"Frishta *jan*," Mummy says. "I'm going out to get some food. Look after your brother."

I nod and she leaves.

Mohsen is down for his afternoon nap, so there is not much for me to do but wait for her to come back. That's another thing I can't get used to about this camp – how boring it is. There are no schools or activities. There is no playground or anyone to play with, as most of the kids here are either teenagers or babies.

The only other kid my age here is a Syrian girl, who has four younger siblings, so she is always taking care of them and never has any time to play. I grab my mother's phone, which she has left behind, and resume my game of PUBG. It is a stupid war game all the kids started playing in Moria before I left. I don't even like it. I guess it's fine to play it sometimes. It makes me feel closer to them somehow.

My game freezes suddenly as the phone starts to ring. It is *khala* Kareema.

"Salam *khala jan*, my mother is not here."

"Frishta, it's me."

My heart stops for a moment. The signal is weak, and I can barely hear him on the line, but I recognise his voice instantly.

"Abbas," I gasp. "Are you okay?"

Ay Khuda, I'm so stupid. I curse myself just as I say the words. Of course he is not okay, what am I thinking? The last thing *khala* Kareema told Mummy was that he was in intensive care.

The day of the fight, he'd fallen and been trampled on, breaking a few ribs. There is a sudden pain in my own ribs as I think about it. He was so sedated at the time we were leaving; I never even got a chance to say goodbye.

"I'm fine, Princess." His voice sounds so tiny over the phone, like he is using up his last bit of energy to talk to me. "I'm a warrior, remember? Nothing ever defeats a true warrior."

I can feel myself tearing up. He is trying to be strong, but I know he is in pain. I want to tell him so much but my voice catches in my throat. Instead, we stay silent, listening to each other breathing through the weak signal.

"I have to go now Frishta. Take care of yourself, okay?"

"Abbas?" Before I can help it, more words slip out. "I miss you."

I hang up the phone before he has a chance to respond. *What was I thinking?* I blush, furious at myself. Tears run down my face. After this, I will never be able to speak to him again.

Mummy's phone buzzes and I am afraid to look. I reach for it reluctantly.

"I miss you too."

A gasp turns into a sigh of relief. The tears stop mid-track. And for the very first time since we arrived in Athens, I let myself smile.

5.2 Maryam

Zee, our new Head of Counselling, stumbles into my office.

"Cancel all your sessions today" he says.

When I say office, I actually mean a walled-off space at the back of the clinic's side tent – with its plastic table and foldable garden chairs dumped in the middle of the space – *posing* as an office.

I keep my head buried in my laptop. Zee's always coming up with all sorts of reasons why I should cancel my sessions to pursue his errands and frankly, I am getting a little bit tired of it.

"Why's that?" I ask half-heartedly, without looking up.

"We need you to step in as an interpreter."

"Come on now, Zee," I groan. "You know that's not my job. I was happy to step in when we were understaffed, but you have more than enough Farsi and Dari speakers now, and enough French speakers. So could you please just let me get on with my work?"

"I know, I know, and I wouldn't ask if it wasn't important."

He positions himself right in front of me. Zee has an annoying habit of cornering people until he gets what he wants.

I reluctantly raise my gaze from the screen to his wide, sheepish grin.

"Hear me out, M."

I wish he'd stop calling me M. I wish he'd go away all together. It has been such a long week, and I just want to go home, collapse onto my bed and sleep until the weekend is over. But no chance of that, not while there is something Zee needs.

"It's about this kid who's been under our care. No parents. He's falling off the wagon, and our counsellor has tried everything." He pauses for dramatic effect, then continues. "Stella is the counsellor leading those sessions, and she believes this kid is on the verge of a serious meltdown. But he refuses to talk to her. He's had five sessions with her already."

Recent events in the camp have been enough to drive anyone to have a meltdown, let alone a kid.

"And?" I chime in.

"Nothing, not a peep," he shakes his head. "The other day, though, just as the boy was about to leave, he said something that caught Stella's attention."

"What did he say?" .

"He asked about you. He said if she wanted him to talk, she'd have to get you."

"ME?"

It is not uncommon for people in Moria to ask for me; but for them to refuse to open up unless I am present, – that's a first.

Zee falls silent and gauges my expression, waiting for the right moment to ask what he has been building up to all this time.

"It's a long-shot, I know," he says sheepishly. "But it's the most we've gotten out of the boy in weeks. So, what do you say?"

I hesitate. I would have to rearrange a lot of my work and move up some meetings and appointments. But the thought of meeting this kid and connecting the dots is intriguing. The thought of actually being able to help the kid is the deal breaker.

"Sure, I'll see him."

"Perfect! He is waiting in the counsellor's tent right now."

"Right now? But—"

"We owe you one, M." Zee winks, before rushing out of my tent-slash-office.

* * * * *

As soon as I walk in, I recognise those dark eyes and jet-black hair, though his face is much more worn and emaciated than I remember. The boy from Rubb Hall all those months ago.

"Mahdi?" I say, tentatively, almost as if I am not sure if it really is him.

"*Chetor aste*, how are you, *khanoom* Maryam?" he asks in a small, distant voice.

There are shadows around his eyes. He is still young, yet these months have broken the innocence of adolescence. The horrors he must have seen; the things he must have experienced – they were far beyond the scope of his youth.

"Mahdi, what's happened to you?" I ask.

"I've been having these nightmares," he says simply, looking at his feet.

"Nightmares about what?"

"My mother, mostly. Sometimes one or both of my younger sisters are there too." He pauses. "Look, I don't want to get into it. Just tell your colleague I want some pills to sleep. I just want to sleep and never wake up."

"You know I can't do that, Mahdi." I coo, drawing up a chair next to him.

He is still looking down, but I can see his eyes starting to shimmer with tears.

"Then leave. You're all the same. You pretend you want to help, but when I say what I need, you all ignore me."

His hand is shaking as it reaches for the pack of cigarettes in his jean jacket and pulls one out. Then, remembering himself, he slides it back into his pocket.

"Why did you ask for me, Mahdi?" I ask him, now stern, but not unkind. "If it were pills you wanted, you could have asked the other interpreters."

He opens his mouth to say something, irritated. But then closes his mouth again and falls silent. Not because he is containing whatever he is about to say, but rather because he is tired. Tired of fighting. Tired of lashing out. Tired of hiding whatever it is that is bothering him.

"Never mind," he mumbles, as he stands up and walks out of the room.

I let him go.

The next time, I approach Zee myself. "I want to be on this case. I feel he wants to tell me something, but he is not ready to yet. Does that makes sense?"

"Perfect sense," he nods. "Actually, Stella can't make her session today, but I don't want to cancel on the kid. He's been through enough, you feel me?" For once, I think I do actually feel him. "Can you go instead? Just talk to him, see how he's doing? It's good to be consistent so he doesn't feel abandoned."

"Absolutely," I say.

I pack up my laptop bag and head for the consultation tent. There's Mahdi, sitting on the chair solemnly with his head bowed low, his fingers and thumbs twiddling.

"Where's your friend?" he sniggers, barely raising his head.

"Stella can't make it today."

"Just you then?"

"Am I not enough?" I say, half-jestingly.

"You're not necessary. Neither of you are. Don't you have anything better to do?"

"Suppose I don't."

"You come here, asking about me and all that shit. Why don't you tell me something about yourself first?"

"What do you want to know?"

"I don't know." He thinks about it for a bit. "How old are you?"

"Twenty nine."

"Ya Allah! And you're not married yet?" I ignore his last comment and glare at him, bemused."Sorry. I mean to ask – how come you're not married yet?"

"I suppose I'm not ready."

"Not me," he grins. "I'm going to get married just as soon as I hit 18. And I want five kids, at least! All boys."

"Oh yeah?" I say, grinning "And why's that?"

"They'll be like my own little army. My strong boys, no one will be able to hurt them. I'll make sure of that. I'll kill anyone who comes near them."

His composure suddenly becomes stiff. The smile fades away. His gaze lowers. His mind wanders away to something in the distance, something unpleasant and worth repressing. Something that may have hurt him in the past. Something that will likely continue to hurt him every time it surfaces.

He shifts uneasily on his chair. I did not notice it at first when I stepped in, but the dark circles around his eyes are getting more pronounced. He wipes his clammy hands on the side of his jeans.

"Another dream?" I ask, cautiously.

No answer.

"It wouldn't be so painful if you stopped resisting."

He twiddles his thumbs and fingers. Then, he lifts his gaze up accusingly. In a matter of seconds, his face has transformed from all smiles, to terrified, to reproachful.

"*Shuma chetor mefahmi?*! What do you know about my life?!" he yells. "You strut in here as if you know everything, as if you understand, but you can't even begin to imagine!"

"You're right, I can't." I say in a calm tone, trying to soothe him. "But maybe you can tell me."

Silence.

He is gone again, gazing at nothing. His look is vacant. His mind is wandering. We are quiet for what feels like hours before he speaks again.

"My mother—." His voice catches in his throat." If she knew what I have become…"

I put a hand on his shoulder, trying to keep myself from crying as well.

"Why don't you give her a call?"

"No, I can't." He looks up with broken eyes, stifling a sob. "I won't."

He looks back down at his feet and, only then, lets himself really cry.

It is then that I realise why he asked for me in the first place. I think back to when we first met, when he searched for something in my eyes, something reassuring that would allow him to open up and let his story come pouring out. Despite all the let downs, there is still a glimmer of hope or trust. He still expects something more from me. Something, perhaps, he does not believe himself – or anyone else – capable of seeing through to the end. Something he will not say in so many words; maybe because he doesn't consciously know what it is. He just knows he needs help, and he has asked me to provide it. .

This time, when I let Mahdi go, I head straight for the Missing Persons Unit, located in a caravan at the entrance of the *Olive Grove*.

The eager assistant beams at me through his red vest.

"How can I help?" he offers.

"I need to track someone down in Kunduz, Afghanistan."

His eyebrows shoot up like fishhooks.

"Oh, well that is a little unorthodox. We usually run searches for people reported missing in Europe."

I nod my head impatiently.

"Yes, yes, I know. But this is important. Please."

"Alright, we'll give it a try." He brings up the form on his computer system. "What details can you give me?"

I hesitate. There is not much tangible information I can provide. Except—

Mahdi's police paper, with his unsmiling face photographed in front of the metre tape. His mother's name had been typed up at the bottom. And it had not been just any name. It was unique. Resonating. Not something to be forgotten easily. The word *Aghel* flashes through my mind – it means wisdom in Persian.

"Her name is Aghela Ramazani. Her husband is dead. She has two daughters and a son, Mahdi, who lives here in Moria."

5.3 Zarifa

They say time cures everything. Even the deepest, darkest wounds – that bleed, ooze and fester – eventually scar. And they may fade with time, but they never fully disappear. Because scars serve as reminders of what we have survived.

Moria is that never-fading scar. Not just for me, but for all women who taste the camp's bitterness. The moment we step foot in this camp, we are all touched by something chronic; something that will stay with us forever. No matter where we go, or what our lives become afterwards, it will always be there – colouring every worldview, shaping every decision. Once you have had a taste of Moria's wars, a drink of its inhumanity or a feel for its lack of dignity, you realise that you are always condemned to be a fawn at the mercy of a lion. But we all find a way to go on. We all find a fighting reason. For women like me – who have given up everything and have nothing left to lose – that reason is, most often, the love of our children.

After my abortion, I was bedridden for weeks; furious with my God for deciding I had not suffered enough in my marriage, in my journey to Europe and in this inhumane camp but should be clobbered with this new shame. I had been fighting all of my life and it got me nowhere, and now that I knew no one had my back, I threw in the towel.

Yazna took over my chores; cooking, washing and feeding little Aylin, who no longer had the warmth of her mother's chest to rely on. In the meantime, I lay in a corner, wasting away slowly, wishing for death to come and find me..

That was about the time I started experiencing sharp,

singeing bouts of pain in the pit of my stomach, just below my navel. Pain that made my entire body jolt and my muscles tense. Something razor sharp bore through my guts, drilling a hole in my core, then left me overpowered and numb all over. No doctor could tell me what its cause was or when, if ever, it would stop. I figured that must have been what it felt like in the end, when the world was ready to abandon me. I felt more than ready to let it go.

But then something astonishing happened. One day, when I was lying on my side in the darkness, Milad approached me and patted me gently on the shoulder. I did not move or even turn my head. I could not bring myself to look him in the eyes anymore; it was too painful. Like being forced to constantly revisit glimpses of my past and present failures, always so tantalising and overpowering.

We stayed together in silence for minutes, or maybe even hours, and then he said the words that turned my life around.

"It's not your fault, *madar jan*. You did what you could for me."

His words unclogged a tunnel in my lungs, allowing me to heave a deep sigh, and then start to breathe again. The pain began to lessen; sensation started coming back to my body. I felt suddenly lighter. I could finally break through the bolts keeping me glued to the ground. I could finally spread my new-found wings and fly. I realised all this time that it wasn't God I was waiting for to set me free from my chains. It was my son.

After that, I woke up from my bedridden trance. I sought out psychological support. I went back into the camp and waited in line, day and night, until they signed Milad and Yazna up for school. I took back control of my household: first by taking back my chores, then by being there for my children, and reclaiming my place in this world as a mother.

* * * * *

I sit on a worn, maroon couch, holding my sleeping Aylin close to my heart and silently promise her that I will never deprive her of my warmth again. My eyes follow the cadence of her chest rising and dropping with her gentle breathing. At the Women's Space in *One Happy Family* Community Centre, five other Afghan women sit next to me, or on the carpeted floor, with their head scarves draped loosely over their heads and shoulders.

My therapist says I should get out more, so I make myself come here every other day while Milad and Yazna are in school, to give myself a chance to unwind and get away from the camp for a while.

Roya, the young mother, is leaning back comfortably on the couch next to me as she breastfeeds her pink-faced newborn. Freba, Kareema, Massouma and Mohammad's mother sit cross-legged on the carpeted floor.

They also come here every other day to engage in knitting and incessant chatter about whose ticket has arrived and whose still hasn't; or whose husband is a pain; or whose children are still on the waiting list for school. I usually sit in the corner, observing and listening, letting myself indulge in their lives before having to return to my own.

"They offered us our ticket today, my husband's and mine," Freba says, never once lifting her gaze up from her jangling needles.

Though she is not new to knitting, the act of looping the yarn around her needle always requires her full visual attention.

"We were supposed to leave this evening with the Heydari family. But I refused because Parwana's ticket has not arrived yet. That good-for-nothing husband of mine tried to convince me to leave our only daughter behindand go to Athens anyway. He says she is 20, she is married and has her own life. He says her husband can take care of her. Can you imagine? His only daughter!"

The other women tsk and tut and shake their heads disapprovingly.

"Well, you go if you want to, I told him. *Yallah*, go! I'm going to stay with my Parwi."

The women buzz in agreement; some even lifting their eyes to give their friend a well-deserved grin for taking a stand against her husband.

Fatima, a woman in her mid-20s, walks in, beaming with a box of sweets in her hand.

"Good afternoon, ladies. I have *baklava* for everyone!" she says in a high-pitched tone.

"What's going on, Fatima *jan*?" asks Freba, still enthralled by her alternating rows of pink and white stitches.

"Well, I am here to tell you all," She flashes a gold ring with a gleaming white stone and squeals. "I'm ENGAGED!"

The women shriek. Some hop up to hug and kiss Fatima and grant her well wishes. Even I lift my head slightly to offer her a congratulatory smile.

"Thank you *khanooma*," Fatima says. "But I have a little problem. What if he thinks—"

"What?" the women sing out in a chorus.

"What if he thinks I'm not, you know," she pauses, looking for the right word and blushes. "A *girl* anymore?"

"Are you not?" Roya gasps. She cradles her newborn daughter, trying to get her to go down for a nap.

"Of course I am! It's just that, recently I have heard people saying some women don't bleed their first time..." Fatima's voice trails off, as her cheeks burn hotter.

"It's true. I've heard it too," Freba muses, gaze still on her knitting.

"So here is what you do," Kareema begins, with that typical sly smirk and twinkle in her eyes that means she is about to reveal one of her secrets. "On your wedding night, have a bottle of red nail polish handy. And if you don't bleed, just as soon as you are done and your husband gets distracted cleaning himself off, dribble a few drops of the nail polish between your thigh and around your privates. Then there you have it! Your broken hymen!" She wiggles her eyebrows with pride.

The women throw their heads back and laugh resoundingly. All except for Massouma *khanoom*, who looks in my direction with a stern and bemused expression on her face, to which I nod sympathetically. She is, after all, older and more conservative than the other women here.

"Bite your tongue, Kareema. What kind of talk is this, may God forgive you," Massouma rebukes.

"Oh, come on, Massouma *jan*, we are all women here," Kareema returns.

"So, what is it like? Having sex?" Fatima asks eagerly.

Asma saunters in, like she owns the place, and drops her shoulder bag in a corner.

"*Salam Alaykum.*"

Asma is one of the new arrivals in the camp. She is here with her husband Amir Ali and her baby boy Basir. She is usually seen grinning and in high spirits. I pray that she remains this way.

"I left Basir in the nursery with the other children, so I thought I'd drop in," she smiles. "What are you all talking about?"

Kareema grins mischievously and raises an eyebrow.

"Sex," she says.

"Sex, sex, sex," drones Asma, rolling her eyes. She loosens her headscarf and lets it fall around her shoulders, then sits on the sofa next to Fatima and Roya. "I just don't understand how anyone can enjoy it. My husband wants to have sex all the time, and I always end up making excuses so he leaves me alone. I don't know what to say anymore!"

"Well, do you love him?" Fatima asks curiously.

Asma laughs as she grabs a *baklava* and chucks it into her mouth.

"He's a good man, *wallah*. He has always been good to me and our son."

"But do you *love* him?" Kareema insists.

Asma hesitates and now, feeling cornered, genuinely considers the question for what seems like the first time.

"I am sure I did once," she muses. "When we were back in Mazar; when love was still fresh and life was still lived on impulse. But now, to tell you the truth, I am not even sure what love is."

The women fall silent.

"What's love got to do with it?" Mohammad's mother breaks the silence. "*Khoda shahedeh*, as God as my witness, I was only a girl of 13, maybe 14. I remember I was sitting with my legs stretched out and my back leaning against a tree, dozing in the summer's heat, when my mother, God rest her soul, appeared out of nowhere and shook me awake. Her face radiated a light of happiness that I had never seen before. She always had an unreadable face, but even if there was an expression on it, it certainly wouldn't be one of happiness. She handed me a bundle of new clothes, some heavy silver chains and a few gold-plated bangles. *Yallah Ghazali, try these on for size. We don't have much time,* she said, beaming from one ear to the other.

What for, madar jan? I asked..

Pir Ahmady's son has asked for your hand. You will be

married on Friday, with God's blessings.

"Pir Ahmady's only son, Akbar *agha*, was a man in his late 30s. I cried so hard, my eyes turned bloodshot. Throughout the entire wedding day and night my head pounded, and for weeks after. But no one cared. They sang and danced as if the bride was just a centrepiece. It was, after all, a union of tribes and that was much more important than anything as fickle as a teenage girl's misery."

"No, *azize* man, not like that.—" Mohammad's mother stops short and reaches out to help Fatima, who is trying to busy herself with knitting a scarf. "You are going to be a married woman and a mother soon after that, *inshallah*. You need to learn how to knit properly. Take your needle and stick it through the loop and now *under* the other one. Good. Now take your yarn and wrap it around the bottom needle and pull it through the middle; just like this. There you go! *Mashallah*, you are a fast learner."

"Anyway," Mohammad's mother continues. "Now Akbar *agha* just lies there in the tent feeling sorry for himself all day and all night while I do all the work. And whenever I speak up, he tells me if I am not happy, I should go and file an official complaint to the police. I accepted him and all the burdens he carried when I was just a girl. I squandered years of my youth, trying to keep a family I was forced into in one piece. And now that his beard has grown long and dishevelled and his hair has turned white, now after all these years, he expects me to go and file a complaint about him?"

The other women have stopped knitting. Some wipe away a few tears that have gathered in the corner of their eyes; others stifle a sob catching in their throat. All of them are moved. Mohammad's mother, on the other hand, is unperturbed as she uses one needle to scoop off rows of loops from the other needle.

"You may look at me and think I am over 50 years old, but

wallah I am only 37," she says, attempting a smile. "The years have beaten me down and all I have to show for them are the fine lines around my mouth and the creases around my eyes."

"Just leave him then," Kareema jumps in. "I will file for divorce once we are done with the asylum procedures and my sons get their papers."

"*Haram*, you young women have no values," tuts Massouma *khanoom*. "Divorce is not the answer to everything. My husband beat me so hard the other day, I blacked out. The paramedics came, and as much as they asked me how I had lost consciousness, I refused to tell them. Marriage is a sacred union, and whatever happens between a husband and a wife, stays between the husband, the wife, and their God."

"*Khala* jan, if you want to stay in an abusive relationship, that is your decision," Kareema darts back. "But don't come preaching to the women here to do the same. *Wallah*, my husband isn't even abusive; he is a good man deep down inside. But so what? When there is no common understanding, no respect. When we are like perfect strangers living under one roof, what's the point? Neither of us are happy."

Roya, who is swaying her baby gently from side to side, cuts in.

"Come now, Kareema *jan*, you know as well as I do, Afghan women don't know the meaning of the word *happiness*."

The air grows sombre, filled only with the clattering of knitting needles. Fatima, the bride-to-be, now looks disheartened, with her needles held defeatedly up in mid-air.

Asma claps her hands together, breaking the momentary daze.

"Put on some music, let's dance," she commands.

She lifts herself up to her feet and switches on the speakers, synchronising them with her phone. She pulls Kareema up as well, drags her to the middle of the room, and together they begin to twist their hips and curl their hands to the sounds of Afghan music.

Fatima is up next, shaking her head and her arms as a smile finds its way back onto her face. Even Roya leaves her swaddled baby sleeping on the sofa and pulls me up to join the party. With Aylin still fast asleep in my arms, I let myself go and begin to move my hips to the beats. One by one, we all stand up until everyone is dancing, all except for Massouma *khanoom*, who merely sighs disparagingly.

Laughter soon follows and the air's heaviness fades in such a contagious way that even Massouma cannot help but grin at the sight us.

It dawns on me then, that all of these women have scars of their own. Some, I know about; while others do a good job of concealing theirs. And yet they still come to this space and find a way to heal in each other's company. From the outside, this may look like a bunch of women letting their hair down and dancing to forget about their woes for a while. But what it actually is, is a room full of warriors finding a way to keep fighting and to survive.

Asma steals over to her phone to change the song.

"This next song is dedicated to our beautiful bride-to-be. Our sister, Fatima *jan*."

The beats erupt and the women form a circle and begin to shimmy, twist their chests and torsos, and sing along to the words. By the end of the song, we have all danced so hard that I collapse onto the sofa, wiping away the sweat beads from my forehead. The others let their bodies slump onto the floor.

Fatima collapses next to Massouma *khanoom*, who never moved from her spot on the floor.

"*Dokhtaram*, my daughter," says Massouma, as Fatima catches her breath. "Here is some advice from someone who has been married for 20 years."

She loops the yarn with such precision and experience that makes us all lean in closer to listen to the wisdom she is about to impart. When Massouma notices the silence, she lifts her chin and gazes around the room, indulging in our attention.

"If you want a long-lasting marriage," she begins, then pauses for dramatic effect. "Never stop knitting."

Her head drops back to her craft, as her needles clink and clank against each other, stitching a new, intricate design.

5.4 Abe

I finally worked up the courage to give Shahgul a call. Not because I expected anything to happen, but more because I thought talking to her would give me a sense of closure.

She spoke casually about the camp she was in and about the kids. Frishta was learning English and Greek; Mohsen was starting football practice soon, and he had vowed to become just as good as his *kaka* Abolfazl.

I didn't try to explain why I had dodged so many of her calls and she never tried to reproach me for it. I told her I missed them, and she said they missed me too. Then we said goodbye, but not in that emotional, attached way we had uttered our goodbyes the last time. More in a way that meant we both silently acknowledged our paths had diverged so much now that all we had left in common was our past. All we had left to talk about was Moria. A relationship based on that could, sadly, have no future.

After that phone call, I gained the courage to do something else I had been wanting to do for a long time. Against everyone's objections, I resigned from my post as community representative.. Even though I am still doing a decent job, despite my recent spouts of depression, I was getting too caught up in other people's problems, leaving no time or energy to work on myself.

I am still willing to step in to help break in the new representative, a young nervous guy with not much experience but overall, I have let go of the official post and feel much lighter since.

The next step is to look for a way out. The guys say, because

I speak English, it shouldn't take me long to find a job – an actual paid one – that will help keep me occupied. Eventually, I'll save up enough money to rent my own place, and get out of this camp once and for all.

Step by step, I feel like I am ready to move on with my life. Because I am finally ready to admit to myself that life does go on, even without the person I loved more than anything. Even in a place like Moria.

I hurry back to the tent before curfew hits, with groceries in hand. It is the end of the month and they have charged all of the refugees' cash cards, so I got stuck in the endless lines for the cash machine to make a withdrawal, and then again at the supermarket. The guys must be getting worried.

I move the blanket covering the slit in the front of the tent and tread in to find four men, sitting shoulder to shoulder, with their backs slumped against the frail fabric of the tent. Navid and our new roommate, Saeed – a young man from Kabul who just arrived last week – play cards, while Hamed and Gul Agha busy themselves with their phones.

The only source of light in the tent is a dim bulb hanging from wires just above their heads. But even that keeps flickering on and off as the fuse outside makes uncertain humming and buzzing noises. This does not unsettle the men; they go about their evening as normal. They are so delved into what they are doing, no one even takes notice of me at first.

"Three Queens," smirks Saeed, flashing a wide dimpled grin along with the cards in his hand. "Beat that!"

"Not so fast, *joonam*," says Navid. His unkempt beard gleams silver and black in the dim light as he turns over his cards and locks eyes with his opponent. "Four Aces."

Saeed throws his cards on the floor.

"No matter," Navid scowls at Saeed, not unkindly. "You're still just learning." He wipes away the sweat drops from his brow before collecting the cards.

It's the peak of summer in Moria. The plastic tarpaulin over our tent offers no insulation against the increasing heat, even in the evening.

"Abolfazl!" exclaims Saeed.

Hamed playfully snatches one of the bags out of my grasp.

"What did you bring us? We are starving!" he demands.

At first, I frown at the two of them.

"It's Abe." Then, I smirk and set the other bags down. "See for yourselves."

Hamed is the first to rummage through the items, followed soon after by Saeed. Then his eye catches a glimpse of something. Grinning widely, he pulls it out with some difficulty. A bottle of red wine.

"*Say kon*, will you look at this, gentlemen?" jests Saeed. "Abe has brought us a surprise!"

"*Ya Ali*!" Navid's brow twists into a frown. "Alcohol? You should be ashamed." I shrink as Navid glares at me. "I should have taken my chances when they offered me to live in that caravan of drug addicts, *wallah*," he scoffs.

I shrug.

"The times are so dark, I thought I deserved a break." I wink at him and fish out two beers for Hamed and Saeed... "And I'm dragging you all down with me."

Even Navid gives in and helps himself to another can of beer. But there is still one man who continues to sit quietly in the corner, without so much as lifting his gaze.

"Gul Agha, what will you have?"

Gul Agha is composed, keeping to himself, fiddling with his phone like an engineer meticulously trialling his invention for the first time. The light reflects off the corner of his lean glasses and his prematurely grey-flecked hair betrays the hardship he has endured in his lifetime.

Only the popping of the cork off the wine bottle makes him glance up from his phone, and inch closer to our circle. As if reading his mind, I pour him a glass of the wine branded *Cleopatra*. Gul Agha plucks the glass readily from my hand and takes a tentative sip. He swishes the wine around in his mouth first and then, satisfied with the taste, gulps down the rest of his glass. It takes a few more glasses for him to travel back in time.

"The taste of this wine reminds me of my first love in Mazar-i Sharif," he remarks, placing the half-empty glass down on the floor next to his feet.

I rip open a bag of crisps and offer it to the others.

"Tell us about it," I prompt.

Drowning in other people's stories has become a hobby of mine. The more I hear, the less alone I feel.

"Her name was Tamana. I was just a boy then, no more than 15 years of age," begins Gul Agha "She was two, maybe three, years older than me. We were distant relatives; second or third cousins or something like that. I'd only seen her at family gatherings, even though we didn't live that far away from each other."

"One night, we were celebrating something. It might have been *Nowrooz* or something else, and I don't know how it came to pass that we were left entirely alone in the house with a bottle of wine at our disposal. So, the two of us drank it up, the whole thing, and it made us so giddy that we talked for hours. What we talked about, I don't even know, but we suddenly seemed to have so much to say to each other.

Everything that had not been said over the years came gushing out after a few mere sips. I am not sure how or why but that night, we fell in love."

"From then onwards, I made sure to see Tamana every day. We didn't always get a chance to speak, so I would stand behind a brick wall across the street from her school every afternoon and waited for her to come out. And when she did, I would smile at her, and she would let her eyes do the smiling for her, before lowering her head and pacing away. She had to be discreet, as she was afraid of being discovered by her schoolmates."

"This little arrangement of ours went on for about a year. Sometimes, when the coast was clear we'd go somewhere together and just sit down and talk. She would tell me what she was learning in school and I would just listen, hanging on to her every word. Other times, a mere exchange of glances would suffice to send my heart fluttering for the rest of the day."

"One day, I was waiting in my usual spot and I counted about a dozen girls coming out of the building. Tamana was not among them. It was strange. She was usually one of the first to leave; impatient to see me. I waited a while longer and finally, when everyone had left, she paced rapidly out of the door. But she kept her head low and made her way home without looking up at all."

"The next day, I went by her school again and waited. This time, she did look up but only for a second and no longer with that expression of mischief or yearning, but rather a sense of heartache or even shame. Quickly after, she dropped her head down again and ran back home before I could follow her."

"Something was wrong. I grew anxious, went over it in my head for a while before heading back home. I tried to convince myself that it must be because she'd fallen ill."

"That day, I found out she was getting married. I was so heartbroken, I didn't know what to do. I couldn't tell anyone that I loved her. I was nothing; less than nothing. The man she was marrying had a name, a job, and I was just a teenage nobody with no prospects for a future."

"So the next day, I didn't go to her school. It hurt too much to see her. I spent a couple of days on my own after that, only to realise not seeing her was even worse. I went back one day and waited, and it was she who didn't turn up this time. I went again the next day, and the next, but she stopped going to school. Maybe she finally gave up on me. Maybe she was settling into the idea of being a married woman and starting to grow fond of her husband-to-be. The thought was painful but comforting at the same time. At least it meant she was happy."

"But I was wrong. A few days later the news reached my family that Tamana had killed herself. Her parents couldn't begin to imagine why she had done such a thing just as her life was beginning to take off. But I knew why," Gul Agha swallows hard. "She still loved me and couldn't bear the thought of being with another."

Gul Agha pauses for a moment, his expression stoic, then adds, almost as an afterthought:

"It was all so innocent. We were just a couple of kids. But we really did love each other."

He falls silent abruptly. His gaze is blank.

Stunned into silence, we stare at him and then at each other as Gul Agha calmly picks up his glass and sips his wine again. The story is over; that much is clear, and there is no reopening the gateway to that particular memory.

Hamed and Saeed fidget, waiting for a sense of closure that never comes. But I am still, composed, lost in my own thoughts. Unlike the others, I have come to understand that there can be no closure for Gul Agha. There are some stories that can never have an ending, not really. When it comes to love and loss, you never really move on. You never forget your first love but you do, eventually and inevitably, move forward, because that is the only way to go.

Maybe one day, Shagul will become for me what Tamana has become for Gul Agha. Maybe she will be a figment that still taints my existence on some level, but one that can only be fully unchained by the taste of an inexpensive bottle of wine – or in my case, the smell of freshly baked *naan* in the morning. Maybe one day, when I have finally left this place, made a life for myself, got married and had children of my own I will think of her as a part of my identity, someone who made me into the man I finally became. Someone who made me not dread my life, my past, or my name. But rather, someone who taught me to be proud to be who I am. To be proud of this Abolfazl.

Gul Agha drains the last bit of wine in his glass, retreats back into his corner and continues playing with his phone. Saeed finally breaks the silence as he picks up the deck of cards and shuffles them nonchalantly.

"Gentlemen," he says, glancing up at the expectant pairs of eyes around him. "The name of this game is *Dozdakan*. The winner is the one who lays down all his cards first."

"Isn't it always?" I say, half to myself, with a ghost of a smile. "Hand me another beer."

5.5 Mahdi

Dum-daba dum-daba -dum.

There is a roll of fingers on the *tabla*, a strumming of guitars and a melody of synchronised flutes played in harmony. The kids' band meets once a week, every Friday, to connect, play and learn music in the classroom in *Section B*.

Samira sings with a soft quiver in her voice.

"*Sarzamin-e man,*"

She drowns out the music, not because she's loud or pervasive, but because whenever she sings, all other sounds fade out in comparison. I can barely even hear the sound of my own guitar.

I didn't want to take up the guitar at first, but Samira talked me into it. Whenever I begin to strum and sing, it takes me back to my earliest childhood memories, when my mother played my grandfather's sitar and sang country songs. That was before the Taliban came. When music was still permitted in our village.

Every time I hold this guitar, I feel as if I am gripping the key to my own soul, bare for the rest of the world to see. And for once, I am not afraid to put it on display. Among the beats, strums and synchronicities, music is a reminder for all of us that even life in Moria can begin to feel bearable.

"*Khasta khaste az jafayat.*"

We all sing Jawed's anthem in chorus. The song we remember him by. The song we dedicate to his memory in every class.

I know I froze at the time, lala jan, but I want you to know, I have never stopped singing it ever since. And I promise I never will.

"*Sarzamin-e man, bi soroodo bi seday-e.*"

Samira mouths the words meticulously, while strumming her guitar. There is something about this girl – with her glitter curls and pursed lips – that always reminds of the first hint of *bahar narenj* or orange blossoms in spring and the first day of *Nowrooz,* all at once.

In the corner of my eye, I catch her headscarf falling back across her shoulders, revealing strands of her thick wavy hair. She is so into her music that she does not even stop to adjust it. I can't help but smirk to myself as a thought crosses my mind.

Man, if her mother saw her now.

She stops for a moment and smiles, showing off her perfect teeth.

"What are you smiling at?"

Her eyes sparkle as she glares at me in jest, turning my knees into rubber. Beautiful though she is, something about her strumming still sounds off.

"It's D Minor, then A Minor again," I whisper in her ear.

I am learning to master the A Minor chord. It is a chord I avoid most of the time. The *Azaan* calls to prayer back home were in A minor. The soundtrack to my childhood, as I played in the fields with my sisters while my mother sang, was also in A Minor. Even the low-key melancholic pitch of Jawed's voice in the mornings was somehow in A Minor. It's as if everything that went wrong in my past was always themed by a perpetual A Minor, like a jammed key on an antique grand piano that just wouldn't stop playing.

Somehow, watching Samira pluck the chord with such ease, and hearing the words of the song just fall out of her mouth like a waterfall, is beginning to redefine the chord. It's as if the curse of the past is starting to lift as I sit back, play along and let the note dance in the backdrop of my mind.

My phone vibrates in my front pocket. I fish it out, up to

the point where I can see the screen only. *Unknown number.*

I push the phone back into my pocket and press my fingers down on the strings again, ready to strum along with the band. The phone keeps vibrating. I let out a deep sigh, lay down the guitar on my chair and make my way quietly out of the classroom.

"*Bali?*"

No response.

Static noise.

"*Bali?*" I say again, this time more sternly.

My chest tightens as a familiar voice, however faint it may be, crackles over the receiver.

"Mahdi? Is that you?"

Worn and aged, for sure, but no doubt it is her.

"*Madar jan.* How did you—?"

Her voice comes out in ripples.

"Mahdi, *bachem.* Are you okay? Are you safe?"

"Yes, *madar jan*, everything is fine. Don't worry."

"Mahdi, why haven't you called?" Her voice is wrought with concern, and suddenly, the guilt of the past several years numbs my entire body.

"I was going to..." I stumble on the words.

I can't tell her that I couldn't bring myself to face her in even worse condition than when I was taken by the *Talib*. I couldn't bring myself to tell her everything I had done just to stay alive. I couldn't tell her that every memory I had of the past few years seemed like a lifetime ago, like pieces of someone else's story ingrained in my mind; like a folk tale that you remember only in fragments, and whose moral has been long forgotten, making it worthless altogether. I couldn't tell her that somehow, she had become part of that fragmented story. The story I wanted to pretend was someone else's. The story I wanted to forget.

"I'm sorry," is all I can manage.

I wait in silence for her to reproach me. I know I deserve it. I deserve far worse than her contempt after everything I've put her through. But she says nothing.

"*Khuda ro shukr, alhamdulillah* that you're okay, my son. Where are you now?"

I hesitate, before confessing what I've been covering up for months; the token of my failed attempts.

"Greece. I didn't make it to Germany."

I look down at my feet and purse my lips in shameRed blotches begin to form on my skin as I anticipate her disappointment.

But all she says is:

"As long as you are safe, my son."

I sigh, suddenly relieved. There is something about the tone of her voice that soothes me instantly. Even after all these years, I can just be a kid around her.

"How are Sara and Somaya?" I ask, more casually.

"Sara is learning how to do embroidery now. We are all very proud of her. And Somaya is the same little troublemaker she always was. I swear that girl will never grow up."

I smile to myself as I try to picture my little sisters, and how they must have grown.

"I'm so sorry—"

My voice starts to break. Before I can go on, my mother cuts in.

"I am proud of you, Mahdi."

My eyes fill up with tears and I swallow back a sob.

"I have to go now. The girls will be back home any moment."

"*Madar jan?*"

"Yes?"

"I love you."

"I love you too, *bachem*."

I take a moment to let sadness and relief wash over me, before dabbing at my eyes with the back of my hand.

When I step back into the classroom, I feel lighter and more at ease than I have felt for years. I sit back down beside Samira, positioning my guitar on my lap.

"Is everything okay?" she whispers.

I smile, this time, not in that smug pretentious way, but in a genuine way – from the heart.

"Never better." I fish a cigarette out of the pack in my pocket and twirl it between my fingers. "What do you say we cut class and go for a stroll? Just you and me."

Samira's mouth gapes. Her eyes dart back and forth between my face and the cigarette.

"*Madar jan* would kill me," Samira stutters.

"I understand," I nod, trying to hide my disappointment.

Her face breaks into the biggest grin I have ever seen.

"So we better make sure she doesn't find out."

"Come on," I wink at her.

Her cheeks turn rosie pink in response. Then I take her by the hand and lead the way out.

5.6 Frishta

I am alone. Mummy is out with Mohsen, but I didn't go with them. Mummy says we should avoid going out if we can because a new virus is killing people all over the world. The only reason she took Mohsen is because he wouldn't stop whining like a big baby.

Khala Tayeba and her boys have left for good too. They packed all their belongings one day and left without even saying goodbye. But I am okay to stay in the room by myself.

All I want to do lately is to play on Mummy's phone anyway, counting down the minutes until sleep so I can wake up the next day and do nothing all over again. Life in this camp is so boring.

I pick up the phone to start a new game, but before I can do so, the phone vibrates. *Incoming video call.* I accept the call and watch as a masked face comes up on the screen.

"Abbas!" I yell, thrilled to see his face – or half of it, at least.

"Frishta, my Frishta," says Abbas, smiling.

At least I think he is smiling. I can't be sure, because of the light blue mask covering half his face. He looks like a doctor. Apparently, they have been giving out masks to the people in Moria since they found a few positive virus cases in the camp.

"How are you feeling?" Igrin.

"Great, now that I am talking to you," he winks..

I blush suddenly and somehow hope it will not show up on camera.

"We have to wear masks here too," I pout. "I hate them. And we're not allowed to go out very much. Not that there is a lot going on around here anyway. It's so boring. What's it like over there now?" I'm blabbering. I should make myself stop.

Abbas raises one eyebrow in a way that is both funny and charming.

"Let me give you the grand tour," he says.

He steps out of his tent and makes his way out into the open. He tilts the phone's camera, lifts it up and fixes the angle on tent 976.

"There's our old tent!" I squeal, a little more excited than I thought I would be.

"Yep. A new Arab family lives here now. They have so many kids, I think they have beat us Afghans in our child-making record."

I giggle. I had forgotten how funny he makes everything sound.

He then walks up the slope, angling the phone all the way up to show me the fenced barrier at the very heart of the *Jungle*. It was a playground that children used to go to, but now families stand behind its chain-link barriers, looking heartbroken and angry.

"What's that place?" I ask, horrified.

"An isolation centre." He shakes his head disapprovingly. "They have started forcing crowds of healthy people to stay in quarantine, telling them they are infected."

My jaw drops.

"But why?".

"Who knows? Maybe just because they can." He shakes his head again. "They send some big shots from Europe over from time to time. They come and walk around the camp. Sometimes they listen to people's stories and say they are sorry, but they could have never foreseen something like COVID-19. But that doesn't really help us, does it?"

I remember when Mummy first talked about coming to Europe. *They will save us there,* she would say, with the brightest eyes. *The Europeans will save us.*

No one will save the people of Moria.

"You're not going to like this." Abbas hesitates for a moment. "But there are talks of fighting back."

I gulp.

"Fighting back how?"

"They are saying they are going to set the camp on fire. All of it. Every single inch."

Fire. The memory still burns fresh in my mind. The acrid smoke setting my lungs ablaze. The smell of brimstone stinging my eyes. My brother's screams as he cowered in the corner. Mummy's despondent eyes when she thought she had lost us.

I swallow hard, my heart pounding against my chest.

"Who?"

"I don't know exactly. But it's no joke anymore. It is really happening."

"Abbas, that's awful."

"Maybe, but what choice do we have left?"

As the words leave him, his golden eyes begin to burn bronze. I recall the look on his face when he ran into the angry mob. I shiver all over.

"Abbas, please be careful." I plead, my voice suddenly faint.

His look softens when he sees my watery eyes.

"Don't worry, Princess. I'll be with mum and dad the whole time. Promise."

That calms me down a little bit at least.

A key turns in the door.

"Mummy's back, I have to go."

Abbas and I wave goodbye and hang up. I rush to the door to let Mummy and Mohsen in and help with the grocery bags.

As I go to get washed up for dinner, I can't get the image

of Moria out of my head. Our tent and the tents of our neighbours; the caravan where classes were held sometimes; the asylum services office with that greasy haired lady who conducted our interview; the endless food line. I try to imagine what it would be like if it were all reduced to ashes and dust.

When I come back into the room, I see Mummy and Mohsen staring, unblinking, into the phone screen at a video.

"*Atash*," Mohsen cries, then looks at me with frightened eyes. "*Abji*, sister. Look, Moria is burning!"

My eyes widen in disbelief as I gasp. Mummy snatches up the phone frantically and starts making calls.

It has begun.

Afterword

My friend sent me a photo on WhatsApp recently, of a half barren piece of land, surrounded by expanses of green grass and trees growing on the other side.

"Do you recognise it?" she asked.

"Is that the *Olive Grove*?"

What was once referred to as the *Jungle* by its thousands of residents now looked as unextraordinary as any other stretch of land. Tourists passing by now would not think twice about stopping there, taking pictures or even giving it a second glance.

"Was kind of shocked to see it..." she confirmed. "It's as if nothing ever happened here."

Some time ago, a former colleague and I were discussing how hard it was to talk about Moria with someone who has never been there. Especially now that it has been reduced to nothing, like it never existed in the first place. The reality was so warped; and distorted; and beyond the breadth of normal lived experience, that every time I try to put it into words, I come up short, which, I acknowledge, sounds odd coming from a writer. But I have always relied on writing to be my soul's channel of communication. The words that don't come so easily to me while speaking, come through more fluidly when put on paper. And today's one of those days where I feel I can write straight from the heart.

This book is a message to the world on behalf of every single person who has ever experienced Moria. Those who are still surviving Mavrovouni camp – or Moria 2 – the camp that was built almost immediately after the first Moria burned down. It is not something that easily leaves your conscience.

These stories represent a tapestry of a myriad of communities grieving together, evolving together, and building resilience together. Women, men and children from all walks of life, assembling, forming solid bonds, having heart to hearts; these are the most empowering tools that give people the strength to come to accept the grim realities of Moria – or any other refugee camp for that matter.

I may have conflated characters for the sake of anonymity, and I may have interwoven stories for the appeal of fiction, but what I want every reader to know is that everything in this book is real. Mahdi is the voice of thousands unaccompanied minors who are forced to give up any claims to being a child the moment they decide to make that perilous journey into the unknown. Zarifa represents the hundreds of mothers who have had to delve deeper than anyone in this world to find unimaginable strength to let go of a continuum of physical and sexual abuse for the sake of one day getting their children to safety. Abe is the vision of a young man who grows up in the unnatural circumstances of Moria, by experiencing the perks of falling in love for the first time, and the crushing defeat of having to let that love go. Frishta is the example of strength and resilience demonstrated by all of Moria's children, struggling to juggle the real-life problems of grownups with what it means to just be kids. And then there is my character, Maryam. I owed it to the world to show how aid workers and volunteers can similarly feel the impact of Moria, and go through its five stages on their own terms, without physically living there themselves.

When I came to Greece in May 2017, I became so engrossed in the work and the people in the camps that everything else in my life became secondary. I could not bring myself to understand how different these asylum seekers' lives were compared to the life I had once known. I had little faith in the organisations I worked for and, as a result, I suddenly felt an overwhelming sense of responsibility to give my absolute everything to help them. The world had turned its back on them; and I refused to do the same. But in the process of giving everything I had to their cause, I lost myself.

After spending some time away from refugee camps, I understood why working in Moria became such a traumatic experience for me.I It is not factually correct that Moria was, in fact, the worst refugee camp on Earth. In terms of shelter, food and access to services – however minimal and trying – it was actually better than some of the camps in Greece, let alone camps in the Middle East, South Asia and Africa. But the psychological impact of Moria was so drastic, and so unlike anything you can imagine, whether you are a resident, a volunteer or an aid worker, it might as well have been the worst.

As a humanitarian worker, my identity was constantly under scrutiny. When the asylum seekers were understandably disappointed in the establishment, there were times they unleashed their frustration on anyone wearing a vest. That meant my colleagues and I would get caught in the crossfire, and I couldn't help but take it personally when that was the case because I felt they were attacking my motivation. I wanted to tell them: *you have no idea what I gave up to be here. You have no idea what being here has done to me; what it is still doing to me.*

Even as a witness, Moria changed me. I went through the five stages along with everyone else: *Stage 1:* the *shock* of observing people's utter disbelief and disappointment upon their arrival in the camp. *Stage 2:* The seething *anger* flaring up in my core every time I was falsely accused of being one with the establishment. *Stage 3:* The heavy load of *guilt* I had to carry around every time I was forced to say something along the lines of, "I'm sorry, I can't help you with that." Or every time I felt that no matter what I did, or how much time, effort and heart I put into it, it was never enough.

Then, there was *stage 4:* My *depression.* I felt Moria's impact full throttle when I was already at the lowest point of my life. I had just ended a six-year-long relationship, and that was just one of the many sacrifices I had made to be there on my humanitarian mission. That was when I started to spiral deeper into solitude.

So, it was not so much that Moria caused my depression, it was that Moria reaffirmed it; it made it permissible. Moria paved the way for my mind to say it's okay to feel defeated. When every day was a struggle for self-justification; when every day I felt I had to keep my shield all the way up to protect myself from the women who came crying to me and asking for my help, help that I could not always give. When I received those reproachful glares, those bursts of anger and silent rebukes, every time I was spotted trudging into the camp with my vest on full display. When children came running up to me, all hugs and smiles, desperate for someone – anyone – to care. All it took was one moment of complete vulnerability to thrust open the door to my unmaking. Something clicked in me as if to say; *it's okay; stop fighting. Just give in and let it consume you.*

What I realised eventually was that, at the end of the day, I became depressed because I was disappointed in myself. It was because I did not understand why I chose to sacrifice everything I knew for the sake of trying to make a difference. Or why I had chosen that, for my life to make any sense, I had to play the part of a hero. It was because I put my humanitarian mission first, and my personal life second.

In the midst of all the clamour and chaos, I began to forget who I was and doubt why I was there in the first place. You see, being a humanitarian worker on the field deprives you of any time for reflection. Everything always happened so fast in Moria, that my life became a constant series of impromptu reactions, until at some point, I suddenly woke up to find myself too deep in the middle of a mental health crisis with no idea how to get out.

But eventually I did find a way out. And here comes my stage 5, *acceptance*. Writing this book for me was not only an attempt to overcome that conversational gap that has defined my life for the past four years. More than that, it was my therapeutic scapegoat, an act of self-compassion, self-redemption even; a way for me to continue on the path of healing by standing by the choices I made, the experiences that defined me, and to give myself permission to fully immerse and reflect on the alternate reality that is Moria.

This book is every ounce of me coming to terms with the fact that the world is defined by injustice, and as one person trying to do right, all I can do is to give what I can without letting it consume me.

I have come to the understanding that true healing means learning to accept the choices I made in life, even though I may not fully understand them, even though they may have been completely intuitive, based on gut feelings and seemingly illogical from a distance. I have come to learn that healing means surrendering, being receptive and eternally grateful for the experiences and inner strength these choices have brought me.

If being human is about learning I am far from perfect, then being a humanitarian worker has been a process of accepting and living with my imperfections. It is a journey, and it is far from over. But like any other journey, I have learned to start by taking my first step forward.

A Final Note

When I started having meltdowns, I decided to keep a diary because I had heard it was one of the many tools people used as a form of self-therapy. Even after my mental health started to improve, I still made sure to check in with my diary every so often – especially whenever anything emotional happens – to just pour my heart out onto its pages.

It seemed fitting to end this book with an extract from one of the entries I wrote in 2019.

25 September 2019

Picture by Bartolomeo Argentino

I had a dream last night, in which I saw two little boys from Moria being so blissful and happy, wandering off into the camp together, arm in arm, as if they were searching for treasure. I asked them what they were doing, and they said that they'd heard there was a magic genie in Moria who granted wishes. And if they found him, they were going to wish to be taken far, far away from here. My eyes filled with tears as I smiled faintly, and said, almost to myself, "I really hope you find him."